Brain and Personality

Brain and Personality

STUDIES IN THE PSYCHOLOGICAL ASPECTS
OF CEREBRAL NEUROPATHOLOGY

AND THE

NEUROPSYCHIATRIC ASPECTS OF THE
MOTILITY OF SCHIZOPHRENICS

BY

PAUL SCHILDER, M.D., Ph.D.

INTERNATIONAL UNIVERSITIES PRESS, Inc.
NEW YORK   NEW YORK

First Paperback Edition 1969

CONTENTS

PART ONE
STUDIES IN THE PSYCHOLOGICAL ASPECTS OF CEREBRAL NEUROPATHOLOGY

PREFACE

In these lectures I have tried to outline my points of view concerning the functions of the brain apparatus. They are based on many single investigations which I have published in German periodicals. I shall try to fill the "gap between the organic and the functional," to make use of an expression of Dr. William A. White, to whom as well as to the other members of the Washington psychoanalytical group I am indebted very much for the interest they have taken in these lectures and the patience with which they have listened to them.

PART TWO
THE RELATION BETWEEN THE PERSONALITY AND MOTILITY OF SCHIZOPHRENICS

PREFACE

These lectures were held for the staff of the Phipps Psychiatric Clinic, Johns Hopkins Hospital, Baltimore, Maryland, when I was there as a visiting lecturer. They are based on the material of this clinic and on studies on this material. I feel deeply indebted to Dr. Adolf Meyer for having had the opportunity of working in this wonderful institution.

PART ONE
STUDIES IN THE PSYCHOLOGICAL ASPECTS
OF CEREBRAL NEUROPATHOLOGY *

CHAPTER I

PROBELMS OF CONSCIOUSNESS †

One of the most important discoveries in neurology in the last few years has been that relative to the centers regulating sleep. This discovery is in close harmony with our experiences of encephalitis lethargica (v. Economo). We know that the patient with encephaalitis lethargica falls asleep and is in a state just like that of a sleeping person. We call that sleep lethargic. In the brains of such individuals one finds a lesion in the gray matter of the midbrain and the diencephalon. There is also a type of lethargic encephalitis in which the patient does not sleep at all, and there is still another type in which the patients are sleepless during the night, whereas they sleep during the day. In close correlation with these experiences with lethargic encephalitis there have also been studied some cases of lesions of the brain due to tumors and similar conditions.

Claude and Lhermitte have shown that sleep is one of the most striking symptoms in tumors of the infundibular region. It is from the region about the posterior wall of the third ventricle that sleep can be influenced. Pötzl has tried to give a more exact localization and believes that the nucleus Darkschewitz and the region around it are the most important points. But there is no doubt that other parts of the gray matter also have a significance for sleep. v. Economo has stated that the center regulating sleep consists of two parts; the one in the more frontal and basal parts regulates the awaking, the more caudal part influences sleeping. My own opinion is that the frontal parts of the gray matter of the third ventricle regulate the clearness of consciousness and the finer order of thinking whereas the distal parts regulate the change between the deeper loss of consciousness of sleep and awaking. Trömner, Spiegel, and Inaba think

* Lectures held before the Psychoanalytic Association in Washington.
† First Lecture, December 11, 1928.

1

that the optic thalamus is the regulating center, but the facts revealed in epidemic encephalitis are not in accord with this opinion. The symptomatology of lesions of the optic thalamus is well known and the coincidence of the thalamic symptoms and disturbances of sleep is rather rare.

When we get sleepy our eyelids droop. There is also a loss of tonus as soon as sleep begins. It is of importance that the supposed regulating centers of sleep should be in close vicinity to the nuclei of the eye muscles and the nucleus ruber which according to Magnus, Rademaker and others plays such an important part in muscle tonus. During sleep there is not only a change in the cortical activity and consciousness but also in the general functions of the body. v. Economo differentiates between cerebral sleep (Hirnschlaf) and body sleep (Körperschlaf).

Sleep is a satisfying function. We enjoy it. We wish to sleep. Sleep begins with the sleeping wish (Schlafwunsch, Forel). This wish is normally as well conscious as unconscious (instinctive). We may abstain consciously from sleep. But finally the instinctive wish for sleep will be the stronger. Unconscious motives may prevent us from falling asleep. The conscious sleep-wish is weak, however, in comparison with the unconscious. In hypnosis the relation between the hypnotizer and the hypnotized person will reinforce the conscious wish so that it gets power over the unconscious wish. There is no doubt that we have on the one hand a well defined psychological function, on the other brain mechanisms which are in relation to this psychological function. Whenever there is a disorder in the sleeping-wish there will also be a change in the function of the organic sleep mechanism.

We do not believe that a center in the brain ever functions in an isolated way. In the end brain activity is always an activity of the whole system. There are only special points which are in special activity. Very likely we always have many points of the cerebral system in action when a special function goes on. I would like to call it a "special figure of irritation or function" ("Erregungs-figur"). This figure certainly is not only static but dynamic. It is like a melody. The figure extends not only in space (the different centers of the brain) but also in time. Sleep not only depends on the subcortical centers just mentioned but also on what is going on in the cortical region. Pavloff has shown that when the conditioned reflex is often repeated and the signal is not followed by the stimulus provoking the unconditioned reflex the conditioned reflex becomes weaker. At the same time the animals get sleepy or really fall asleep. Pavloff supposes that the inhibition concerning the conditioned reflex has spread over the whole cortical region and has thus provoked sleep. I think we have to suppose that the inhibition has gone to the sleeping center of the third ventricle. The sleep wish, either natural or provoked by hypnosis, has certainly something to do with the cortical region but it goes from the cortex to the sleeping center.

In encephalitic cases there is no reason to suppose that the sleep wish is changed but that the (so far) normal wish has not its proper influence on the affected sleeping center.

In cases of neurotic sleeplessness we have no reason to believe that there is serious trouble in the sleeping center, but that rather the sleep wish is contradicted by " unconscious " motives. But this antithesis is too schematic; we have good reason to suppose that in many cases of neurotic troubles of sleep there is also some individual disposition of sleep which makes the neurosis choose this very symptom.

While sleep is going on there is a great change in our consciousness. In some way sleep is the necessary condition for the dream. It is true there are also day dreams, but if we compare them with real dreams we find that consciousness in the day dreams is never altered as much as in dreams. The day dream does not bring forward as primitive material as the dream; there is less symbolization and less condensation. Infantile material does not come out so much in the day dream as in the night dream. In brief: the day dream has the structure of the Preconscious, the night dream the structure of the Unconscious. The sleeping center therefore does not only provoke sleep but it also induces a psychic change. A more primitive state of mind comes back, regression takes place. There is also a relation between a midbrain-diencephalic center and a special state of regression.

But consciousness is not a simple function. Different changes in consciousness may occur. The change in consciousness provoked by a lesion of the anterior part of the gray matter of the third ventricle is different from the deeper loss of consciousness during sleep. There is not only one center for " consciousness " but there are, as Kleist has stated, a series of centers. Distal from the sleep center (nucleus Darkchewitz?) there must be a center the lesion of which produces a more complete loss of consciousness. In encephalitis hemorrhagica superior (Wernicke) we find in connection with palsies of the eye muscles, a loss of consciousness reaching to the degree of coma. In delirium tremens ocular palsies are also common and the sleep following it is a connecting link between normal sleep and the coma in polioencephalitis hemorrhagica superior. In delirium tremens there is certainly also a change in consciousness. Consciousness is not clear. But condensation and symbolization play a minor part. Probably lesions of the more distal parts of these centers impair much more the clearness of consciousness but do not provoke as many condensations and symbolizations as a lesion of the proximal parts.

The most distal parts of this chain of centers have then to do with the clearness of consciousness. Such lesions provoke a deep somnolence. Tumors of the fourth ventricle provoke it. Breslauer's experiments on rabbits confirm this point of view. When he pressed the cortical region there was no change in consciousness; when he pressed upon the medulla oblongata the animals lost consciousness immediately. Knauer and Enderlen obtained similar results.

With Weismann I have observed a tumor of the hypophysis stalk. The tumor was slightly proximal to the sleep steering center. The patient came into the clinic in a state of mental confusion. She heard voices. People were shouting outdoors. She complained that a tube was introduced into her anus. She was always dozing. She was helpless and confused. There was a polyuria, and I am inclined to assume that there was a lesion proximal to the sleep steering center and that the changes of consciousness in the direction of mental confusion were due to this lesion. In patients in whom the sleep center itself is affected or where lesions are distal to the sleep center the impairment of consciousness is more marked.

I also observed a patient who had a tumor of the hypophysis with the symptoms of impotency and impaired vision. He was operated upon successfully. Such operations on hypophyseal tumors, however, do not completely remove the tumor. After the operation he developed a state of anxiety associated with hallucinations. The hallucinations were of the following type: he had a faint feeling of worms crawling on his body. These worms were small, and sometimes he heard little noises like the clicking of scissors. The only way he could obtain relief was to have his brother come into his bed and press himself against his body. These hallucinations and the feeling of anxiety occurred chiefly in the evening before falling asleep. He was sleepy during the whole day.

In this patient again we have a brain lesion which lies frontal to the centers of consciousness. There is not a great change in the consciousness, but still consciousness is altered so much that there are some archaic pictures brought out. There is no doubt that the worms are symbols for the penis. The anxiety is related to his homosexual tendencies and therefore he gets help by pressing his body against that of his brother. The modification in the sexuality is due to the lesion of the diencephalon. Impotency follows. But the change in consciousness may have to do with the fact that the homosexuality now comes out in a symbolic way. The first patient I reported upon had disturbances of menstruation and anal erotism appeared.

In the dream, primitive sexuality comes into evidence. There must be some connection between the function of " consciousness " and the sex organ functions. We know indeed that the sex centers in the diencephalon are near the sleeping and consciousness centers. And whenever we find in the brain two centers near each other there is also a functional connection between them.

The column of nerve structures related to the centers for consciousness is accompanied by the column of centers for the vegetative nervous system. This column also extends from the medulla oblongata up to the region of the optic thalamus. With changes in consciousness we usually find changes in the vegetative system. The opposite is also true. The two focal points for consciousness, the medulla oblongata and the mesencephalic-diencephalic region, are indeed focal points for the vegetative system.

It would be an interesting task to study stupors from a similar point of view. Miller and Richter have made some investigations on these points. But all the problems of sleep of our patients have to be studied as it has not been done up to the present time. I may remind you in this connection that there is a state of complete sleeplessness during delirium tremens, and that many patients with acute encephalitis show psychotic symptoms which are almost identical with delirium tremens. All these patients are not only sleepless but also restless. They show a motor excitement. Whenever the average individual is sleepless he will not be able to be quiet, he will be restless also. Children who have an acute attack of hyperkinetic encephalitis often sleep during the day but become not only restless but excited in the evening and at night. Some of them even get maniacal. These changes in the consciousness centers are connected with changes in the spirit and mood.

Of course these centers of consciousness are not only affected by organic lesions, they are also affected by our conscious and unconscious psychic life. I have reminded you therefore of what is produced by the sleep wish and by hypnosis. Sleep problems are then to be considered as psychological as well as physiological.

These problems of brain pathology and of psychoanalysis are also problems of pharmacology and I shall make a few comments about these pharmacological problems. When I made my studies on hypnosis I found, as have all the others who have experimented with hypnosis, many patients who do not react to hypnosis as one would wish. Therefore, I began to try to help the hypnosis by giving the patient a sleeping medicine beforehand. I started by giving the patient half a gram of veronal an hour or two before hypnosis. Later I gave medinal from 0.5 to 1.0 gram. In some cases it would be more advisable to give paraldehyd immediately before the hypnosis (4–8 gram). It was astonishing how patients who could not fall asleep, who laughed at the procedure when under the psychic influence alone and who could not sleep by the medicine alone, fell asleep when both sleep producing medicine and psychic influence were used. One can therefore say that psychic influence and a drug influence can be added to each other. When we have produced hypnosis completely forgotten material can be brought out.

These centers about which we have spoken have therefore not only to do with consciousness—they must also have something to do with the memory. I have begun to study the amnesias from this point of view and have found out that at least in one or another case of postepileptic amnesia it is possible to bring out what has happened during the dreamy state. An especially interesting group of cases are those of amnesia after alcoholic intoxication. W. A. White[1] in a very interesting paper which appeared twenty years ago, says that these amnesias can disappear under the influence of hypnosis. R. Stern, who has worked with me, found that the amnesia of alcohol intoxication in almost all cases can be made to disappear by hypnosis. In many instances, however, it is necessary to reinforce the hypnosis by drugs.

A further opinion, from a psychoanalytic point of view, is that forgetting is not something which goes on only in the organic life. It is in connection with the process of repression and we have to say there must be a connection between the organic and psychological and chemical influences and the function of forgetting and remembering. Pharmacologists in recent years have studied sleeping medicines from a purely pharmacological point of view and have found out that

[1] White, Wm. A. Mental Dissociation in Alcoholic Psychosis. With B. Sidis, G. E. Stechert, 1902.

two types of drugs exist. One type has its influence chiefly upon the cortex and includes bromide, alcohol, amylhydrate, paraldehyd, etc.; the other type influences the brain stem, barbital, cholesterin, and similar drugs (Pick and his co-workers). When one studies the so-called " organic " amnesias one finds that there are some cases which do not react to veronal hypnosis, but only to paraldehyd. We can thus see that these problems of pharmacology stand in very close relation to purely psychological problems and there is no essential difference between sleep that has been provoked by a sleeping wish and one produced by these narcotics. We know from our psycho-analytic studies that a sleep which is provoked either by cortical or meso-diencephalic sleeping medicine and sleep which is provoked by a lesion of the sleep center as such is closely related. In all types of sleep perceptions that are otherwise forgotten can come into the memory again and we can see that the whole system about which we have spoken is at the same time a system which is in connection with the memory from an organic point of view.

We know that in dreams this forgotten material comes out again and it may be important to remember that there are two systems of memory. The one system is that from which all remembrances come out again as such unchanged, but there is another type—whatever is forgotten always sends symbolic pictures into the memory (cf. Freud). The dream has to do with both systems. I may remind you in this connection that even the so-called primary scene (Urscene) which is at the basis of a neurosis may appear in an unchanged way in a dream. On the other hand most of the forgotten material appears in the dream at first as symbols. When one studies epileptic amnesias from this point of view one will note that forgotten material appears in a completely unchanged way. I believe, therefore, that all the consciousness systems retain at any rate the unchanged memories, but that at the very moment when the functions of these centers of consciousness are going on condensation and symbolization also take place. From this point of view we have to study also all these questions which are in connection with the problem of forgetting the dreams. The dreamy states have an organic and a psychological aspect quite in the same way as these problems. Even hysterical amnesia has an organic aspect. From this point of view we get a different outlook on many problems of psychiatry. But sleep has not only an influence upon the memories, it changes also our attitude toward the world and especially towards other persons. When we speak with a sleeping person, he gets attached to us as much as a hypnotized person does to the hypnotizer. He will even carry out posthypnotic orders. That lovers like so much to sleep with each other is another instance of the close relation between sex and sleep. When we say that love awakens during the night, this saying has some physiological background. Natural sleep as well as the sleep provoked by drugs changes the transference situation.

But let us go back to the pharmacological problem. I must say that we have studied up to the present time too little of what goes on under the influence of drugs. We do not know what goes on under the influence of opium for instance. It would be absolutely necessary to study the dreams which occur under the influence of opium and cocaine in order to get a better insight into the problems of addiction. Drug addicts show changes in their sexuality. According to the investigations of H. Hartmann cocaine may provoke overt homosexuality in those who were not overt homosexuals before. But it is also true that latent or manifest homosexuality predisposes one to become a drug addict and an addict to cocaine especially. I may add that there is a marked change in the motility of cocainists. They get restless, almost choreic, sometimes even really choreatic and they show also a marked change in their states of consciousness. It is proved that this drug has also certainly an influence on the brainstem.

I may repeat here what psychoanalysis knows about the alcoholic. Alcohol sooner or later not only diminishes the potency but changes also the quality of the libido. The latent homosexuality which predisposes to alcoholism (very likely generally to drug addiction) becomes more open. It may appear first as jealousy or even as delusions of jealousy. The alcohol influences consciousness. I may mention again in this connection how often acute alcoholic intoxication impairs the memory. The forgotten material may come out in subsequent alcoholic intoxications or by hypnosis aided by paraldehyd.

Every kind of addiction has its special psychoanalytic and pharmacological aspects as well as its problems of brain pathology. But these problems have also some practical consequences. At first we may ask what type of changes continued sleep can provoke. Continued hypnosis is sometimes very useful in the treatment of a psychosis. We know that veronal has been used for prolonged hypnosis and we should not be surprised if a prolonged hypnosis or a prolonged sleep changes something in the complexes. The treatment by prolonged sleep in schizophrenia and also in mania is based on these considerations. Kläsi has found out that prolonged sleep in schizophrenia often has a very good influence and that patients lose their schizophrenic symptoms. (Kläsi has continued something which many years ago was begun by Wolf.) Kläsi thinks that sleep makes the person dependent on the nursing personnel and because of this feeling of dependence the patient gets a better transference. And in such a way he may be extricated from his narcissistic stage. This idea of Kläsi's certainly is very interesting. Very likely it is not the only reason for the curative effect of the sleeping treatment. The change in the transference is seemingly only the reflection of what also is going on in the purely organic sphere. It is an old experience of the hypnotist that the transference of the treated person gets stronger the more often he is hypnotized. Sleep not only causes a regression to a more primitive stage, it not only changes condensations and symbolizations and opens the way to forgotten memories but it also changes the state of transference. This fact must be considered very important.

The sleeping treatment of Kläsi is, however, rather dangerous. In the chain of consciousness centers, the center which provokes sleep is not so far distant from those centers, lesions of which provoke coma somnolence and death. Deep loss of consciousness is the forerunner of death. And a stronger insult to the centers of consciousness will injure the vegetative column so near to it anatomically and functionally, so that lesions of its deeper parts will lead to medullary death. Ultimately all death comes from the medulla oblongata. The outward similarity between death and sleep is not deceiving. It is physiologically the same apparatus with which both are related. This apparatus extends from the medulla oblongata to the diencephalon. It consists of a chain of centers of consciousness and a related chain of vegetative chains of apparatus among which the apparatus for the sex functions plays a special part. This chain is also connected with the apparatus of tonus and motility. The function of this chain influences the cortical activities. The cortical activities also influence this chain in a very high degree. Sleep cannot be understood if we neglect the psychology of the sleep wish. In the sleep wish one's whole personality comes out. All these centers do not act in an autonomous way. They get in action in connection with life problems, with the situations of real life and our attitude towards them.

CHAPTER II

PROBLEMS OF TONUS

When a person falls asleep the muscle tonus is completely changed. At first the eyelids droop, then the neck muscles and the muscles of the trunk relax. But very often there are some choreic movements before this final relaxation occurs. Sometimes there is a sudden jerk in the semi-sleep state, the person feels as if falling from a high mountain or a tower. During sleep itself a peculiar attitude is not uncommon. The legs are flexed in all joints, the head is bent forward, the arms are flexed and pressed to the body. The individual assumes an embryonic position. It is a position the opposite of that of typical decerebrate rigidity when the extensor muscles are in action. Decerebrate rigidity occurs when a transection is made through the brain at such a level that the brainstem is separated from the red nucleus. It is of great importance to note that the nucleus ruber is near the supposed sleep center. The change in consciousness of sleep is also connected with very well marked changes in muscle tone. And when psychoanalytically we assume that sleep is a regression to the embryonic state the neurology of the sleep position certainly fits very well into the scheme.

We meet similar problems when studying narcosis. In the state of excitation in the beginning of ether narcosis, Weismann and I have found a picture which reminds one of the decerebrate picture. The same picture may be observed in the stage before waking. During deep narcosis almost complete lack of muscle tonus is present.

It may seem far fetched but I wish, nevertheless, to point to the fact that after complete relaxation by death there comes a state of muscular rigidity (although there is no doubt that this rigidity is based on the state of the muscles themselves).

But there is another group of phenomena of tonus which is connected with changes in consciousness. This is the tonus of the postural and righting reflexes of Magnus and de Kleyn. Goldstein uses the term induced tonus (inducierter Tonus). When we turn the head of an animal with decerebrate rigidity, the jaw extremity, that extremity to which the chin is directed, will show an increased rigidity, the skull extremity will show a flexion. The position of the

10

head influences the distribution of the tone in the body. We call these reflexes, reflexes of posture (Haltungsreflexe). An animal with decerebrate rigidity is able to maintain its position, but it is not able to get back into a normal position once brought out of it. This is the function of the righting reflexes, for which the most important center is the nucleus ruber.

We find these reflexes in normal animals, too, but they also can be found in normal men. Goldstein and Riese have ordered their subjects to give way to every motor impulse. Fischer and Wodak have done the same and found that the active or the passive movement of every limb influenced the position of the other limbs of the body especially of the same side. Zingerle has observed the same thing in psychopathic individuals and has spoken about automatosis. They made also spontaneous movements, turned around their longitudinal axis and so on.

In performing these movements the individuals get into a special state of consciousness which is not quite the same as the state of hypnosis. This state of induced tonus is remarkable from many points of view. Whenever, in such a state, we change the position of one leg, for instance, by passive flexion at the hip, then there will be a raising of the arm of the same side. When I turn the right leg inward, at that moment the right arm will also turn inward, and very often the hand will make a movement in the same direction. We therefore can see that the tonus of every limb, even of the entire body and especially the side on which the limb is moved in a passive way, is changed. It goes so far that we might find changes in the position of some parts of the body whenever we move the big toe. Sometimes also the position of the head is influenced by the passive movements of the toes, of the ankle, of the hip and the arm. It is not only true that the head influences the position of the limbs and the body, but also the position of the limbs influences the head and also the other limbs of the same side. One has contradicted Goldstein because he has described only psychogenic phenomena, but I have myself observed cases of cerebellar and parieto-occipital lesions in which the same phenomena were present as in the experiments of Goldstein. Thus I found that passive turning of the head to the right made the cerebellar patient turn around the longitudinal axis. When I turned the foot of the patient outward, she made an outward rotation with her arm and also turned her head to the side to which the passive foot rotation took place. When I made a passive outward movement with her toe, the arm made the same outward movement. It was unquestionably an organic case.   Therefore Hoff and I think there must be some truth in the experiments of Goldstein.   Also this cerebellar case developed a special state of consciousness when these induced reflexes took place.   Whenever those reflexes take place which tend to keep the body in a normal position in space and maintain a normal position between head and trunk a peculiar state of mind will occur.   I have mentioned that we have observed similar changes in a lesion of cortical field 19 of Brodmann.   That is a field which lies between the parietal and occipital lobe.   In lesions of this field we have not only seen active movements of the patients around their longitudinal axis but increased righting and postural reflexes.   When I turned the head of the patient outward, the patient moved the hand in the same direction and began to move around on his longitudinal axis.   We have thus before us many phenomena of so-called induced tonus which are in a very close relation to what one calls consciousness.   We can say now that we know something about the primary centers of so-called induced tonus.   We know that the nucleus ruber plays a very important part in these induced movements but these so-called reflexes of posture and reflexes of righting have centers which extend from the medulla oblongata up to the nucleus ruber.   This system accompanies the system which has to do with consciousness, and we can thus see how every state of mind is in connection with a special state of muscle tonus.   We have proved it concerning the tonus of sleep and for the tonus of the righting reflexes.   There is doubtless a relation between tonus on the one hand and consciousness on the other hand.

Of course we cannot say that the problem of tonus is only a problem of the medulla oblongata and of the brain stem.   We know that there are many other parts of the brain which influence tonus; I have mentioned the parieto-occipital lobe.   But there are also the frontal lobe, the temporal lobe, the striatum and pallidum, the cerebellum and the substantia nigra.   But the primary centers are those accompanying the centers of consciousness.

It is strange that we know so little about the state of mind of a dizzy person.   Whenever one gets dizzy one experiences a direct change in consciousness.   I have observed that patients with an organic dizziness very easily get hysterical and it is sometimes very difficult to distinguish between an organic and a functional dizziness. This very likely has to do with the fact that dizziness provokes a state of mind which makes it easier for functional mechanisms to exert an influence.   But I shall speak about this problem a little later.

At first I wish to make the remark that when I personally felt a little seasick during a storm I got very sleepy and I have heard from others that this is a combination that occurs not infrequently. It may be that between dizziness and sleep there is some relation. Children are rocked in order that they may fall asleep. In one of my cases of Menière's disease every attack was followed by yawning and sleep. During dizziness we find also changes in the muscle tonus. When I recovered from this beginning minor seasickness I felt at the same time that my coördination in going up and downstairs grew much better and we have to consider the problem of dizziness always in connection with muscle tonus. I may remind you of Bárány's experiments in which irrigation of the ear with cold water is used. The subject has a tendency to fall to the side of the irrigation and at the same time we also find a deviation of both arms to that side. But the subjects get at the same time into a peculiar state of mind, and the feeling about the body is changed. The body feels lighter, some parts of the body may feel heavier. Persons who have a lesion of the vestibular system, either organic or functional, fly in their dreams. I have myself with Eisinger observed these flying dreams in patients with a labyrinthine fistula and I also have had under my observation a patient with a cerebellar lesion who, in a dream, visited her friend by flying from one window to the other window of their house. Dizziness not only changes the feeling of one's weight but some people complain that they have queer feelings in their head. One of Bárány's subjects said, " I have a stupid feeling in my head " and we can say that many of the feelings which are in close relation with depersonalization are associated with dizziness.

I may report here an observation of mine. A patient came into the clinic with a complaint that her left side was completely changed and that she did not feel her left side, but she did not show any signs of disturbances of sensibility. She complained only that the sensations did not mean anything to her, or in other words, she presented a picture which showed very close relationship to depersonalization. This was a depersonalization of one side only. The patient had the following organic symptoms: lack of corneal reflexes and a vertical nystagmus, which is a sign of a lesion of the proximal parts of Deiters nucleus. The patient had also a very interesting sleep disorder. She complained that she was very restless during the night; that she was disturbing all the other patients so that she would have to be put in the ward for disturbed patients; she complained at the same time that during the day she slept deeply. The objective observation did not show anything of that kind. The patient slept during the night absolutely quietly and was absolutely awake during the day. But she described a trouble of sleep which as you know occurs in reality in patients with encephalitis who really have disordered sleep. These patients for two or three days fall asleep during the day in a similar fashion to that of a narcoleptic.

What does such a case mean? We can say that we have before us a lesion which is not far from the sleeping center and that her subjective phenomena have the same value as objective phenomena; these complaints about sleep occur in a case where Deiter's nucleus is affected, a nucleus which has much to do with the regulation of tonus. We come to the conclusion that the apparatus which has to do with organic dizziness is at the same time an apparatus which has to do with the appreciation of our own body. There are also close relations between this apparatus for tonus and the apparatus for sleep and both have rather close relations to the appreciation of the feeling of our own body. From a psychoanalytical point of view it is very interesting that we find dizziness in all cases of depersonalization. We can say that when we analyze such a case of depersonalization we find that the dizziness is in connection with a conflict between two tendencies and we can state that neurotic dizziness is the expression of two psychic tendencies which are combating one another, whereas organic dizziness is in connection with different data of our perceptions which do not fit each other. We may find the flying dream, as a symptom of conversion, as an expression of repressed sex wishes, and we may find the flying dreams also in connection with a direct lesion of the nervus vestibularis or of a direct lesion of the cerebellar system. The vestibular nerve is an apparatus which can very easily give symptoms when there is a tendency to conversion. It is important to notice that the nervus vestibularis is one of those apparatuses to which conversion goes over easily. It is not quite clear by what mechanisms the conversion acts on the vestibular nerve. I have made some experiments with J. Bauer in which we gave our hypnotized subjects the suggestion that they were turned around in one direction. Some of these subjects reacted then with their body quite as a person would react who had been really turned around his own axis, and we have drawn from these observations the conclusion that we have to do with psychic influences on the vestibulocerebellar apparatus. Some believe that only our static knowledge is changed by such an experiment and others have had the opinion that we do not influence the vestibular cerebellar apparatus in a direct way, but that we influence only the vasomotor system of the nervus vestibularis. It is possible that these two mechanisms occur together. I personally believe that by suggestion we can influence directly the vestibular-cerebellar apparatus, the nuclei of which are very near to the centers of the sympathetic nervous system and which can be influenced in a psychic way. We know that there is vomiting which comes on as a result of a psychic disturbance. But there is no doubt that in some cases the nervus vestibularis is influenced by a change in the vasomotor mechanism. And there is no doubt either that our knowledge of directions (Richtungsvorstellungen) can be changed by suggestive methods.

I may report in this connection a rather interesting case. When I studied organic dizziness in the ear clinic, a physician came to me with some organic signs of dizziness among which was a slight nystagmus. I examined him from a purely somatic point of view and the result was that I found out that he was a patient with vasomotor troubles which I could demonstrate by choking him slightly. By this change in the blood vessels it was possible to provoke organic vestibular symptoms. Then I told him there was no organic basis for his symptoms and that he was suffering from a neurosis. At the same time one of my psychoanalytic friends called me up and told me that this man was a patient of hers and it was interesting to learn that the immediate cause for this vasomotor trouble affecting his vestibular apparatus was the following: this psychoanalyst had some vasomotor troubles of a Raynaud type that came to the attention of the patient. On the next day he developed the symptoms of dizziness which I have reported.

It is important to know that the nervus vestibularis responds so easily to psychogenic troubles and the response is partly a vasomotor response, but I would insist upon my opinion that the vestibular apparatus can be also influenced in a direct way by psychic events. I mentioned that we find in almost every case of depersonalization symptoms of dizziness which are not only a " representation " but also organic change in the vestibularis as such. Of course dizziness is one of the most common conversion symptoms in the neurosis and when one studies the neurosis from this point of view one will find in almost every neurosis one or the other sign of dizziness.

We have to consider also that on the other hand dizziness can provoke neurotic mechanisms as I have mentioned. Especially when one studies cases with organic ear troubles, one finds many mechanisms which are identical with those one finds in neurotic cases. Patients who get a lesion of the vestibular nerves very often have monocular polyopia which is not of psychogenic origin. This monocular polyopia, this multiplication of visual impressions, occurs very likely in connection with the fact that the motor impulses of the nystagmus exert an influence on the optic pictures. It is interesting from this point of view to study the dreams of patients with organic lesion of the nervus vestibularis, *e.g.,* those with a labyrinthine fistula. In many of these dreams the patients see many objects moving around, people dancing, great masses of people, all of them moving with quick and irregular movements. In these dreams we can see the expression of the influence of the vestibular nerve on the optic pictures by the change of the motor impulses. Very likely the polyopia of hysterics has quite a similar basis. In a patient I have studied I have found out that there was trouble in the equilibrium of the eye muscles in hysterics who have a monocular polyopia. All of these troubles of tonus which come out in nystagmus have at the same time an influence on the optic pictures and on the optic images. This influence is greater where there is at the same time a change in consciousness due to dizziness as such or to some other circumstances (sleep, delirium). The same psycho-physiological problems occur in delirium tremens. We have spoken about these in connection with the problem of sleeplessness. In delirium tremens cases we found multiple hallucinations which were related to lesions of the vestibular-cerebellar apparatus. I have studied this from an experimental point of view irritating the ears of these patients with cold water. When I provoked a dizziness the number of the hallucinated animals increased and all these animals were in greater movement than they were before. I wish to make clear that the nervus vestibularis has to do with tonus, and with consciousness, but also with optic pictures and with optic images and many of the symptoms of the organic psychoses may find their interpretation from this point of view. There is no doubt that it is of great interest that the nervus vestibularis on the other hand is one of the parts of the body that is so specially under psychic influence. That is not only true about the nervus vestibularis, but is very likely true about the cerebellar system. It is also under a special psychic influence. In the so-called hysterical astasia-abasia we deal probably with the imagination of the patient but also with the influence of this imagination on the organic vestibulo-cerebellar system. Every hysterical symptom has not only a " psychic " but also an organic basis. We have to study carefully in which way the cerebellar apparatus can be influenced by emotions. We have spoken about the relation of the nervus vestibularis to tonus and I may add that in some of the Menière cases the patients suddenly lost their tonus. At the moment the dizziness comes on, the patient falls down, his tonus completely lost.

Sudden loss of tonus also occurs in the so-called narcolepsy about which we have to speak now. Narcolepsy consists in brief attacks of sleepiness. These patients fall asleep when standing, when walking, and some of them really fall down. In sleep and sleepiness we find the loss of tonus, which begins in the muscles of the eyes and then goes to the other parts of the body. In these narcoleptic cases there is something else which is of interest and that is that many of them show a change in their tonus under the influence of emotions especially when laughing or when angry. In some cases this emotional loss of tonus is so great that the patients fall down at the very moment they begin to laugh and we come to the conclusion that there may be some close relation between tonus on the one hand and these emotions on the other hand. Not all the cases of so-called narcolepsy are pure organic cases. I have got the impression that in many of these cases the psychogenic factor plays a very important part and is more important than the organic factor. I observed a case of post-encephalitic narcolepsy in connection with hysterical polyopia. It is interesting that the father of this patient had had attacks of hypersomnia too. I believe that the psychic influence which can produce sleep can also produce a loss of tonus and between tonus and psychic, especially emotional, life there must exist a very close relation.

Metzger has exposed children to special types of strong light and has observed that these children reacted to the difference of the light with a difference in the tonus and it was shown that especially the side of the body reacted on which the light fell. The influence of light on tonus is certainly a very great one. In lower animals it has been studied very carefully and one can prove that some insects react with changes in tonus when one directs light into their eyes. In very close relation to this light tonus are the so-called optic righting reflexes. A monkey that has lost his labyrinths still can maintain positions of the head with his eyes open which he cannot maintain if he has his eyes closed. The head of the animal droops when the eyes are closed. We have therefore a light tonus and we can say that there exists a primitive tonic reaction towards light, and a primitive tonic reaction which changes with light. Simlar changes of tonus occur also if sound meets the ear of an individual.

It has been observed by Goldstein, Hoff, and by me in cerebellar cases which have increased righting reflexes that whenever we direct light into one eye of the patient, the patient begins to turn around towards the light in an irresistible way. At the same time there are changes in consciousness and sometimes he turns around completely. The change in the tonus can be proved in a very simple way if we order the patient to perform the past-pointing test. The patient shows past-pointing in the direction from which the light meets his eye. By light and also by sound the whole tonus of the body becomes changed and the whole body turns towards the direction of such an impression. In one case of this type I have observed, I also got these reactions whenever I touched the patient on the side of her face. She turned around to this side in a tonic way. We can therefore say that very likely every impression causes a reaction in a tonic way and we have in the tonic reaction the most primitive, the most instinctive reaction. These primitive reactions go on according to laws which are not so different from the laws psychoanalysis has discovered. If by the movement of the leg I induce a movement in the arm and I check the movement in the shoulder, the movement will come out instead of in the shoulder, in the head. It is interesting to observe the effect, when two impulses of posture are given, one of which is contrary to the other. If, for instance, I turned the left hand outward, the patient turned her head and body to the left. When I took both of her hands and turned them outward, the patient began to move either backward or forward in a violent way. There is an induced movement or induced energy which has to come out somewhere. If it cannot come out in one muscle, it comes out in the muscle which is free at the moment, or we can say this tonic energy, the most primitive type of movement, can be transferred from one muscle to another muscle. We cannot say in such a case the tonic energy is bound to one muscle, but we have to say that the tonic energy will appear in the muscle which offers the least resistance. Very likely these tonic energies are our first reactions to whatever goes on around us. These are the primitive types of reaction towards the world. Generally we react in this tonic way, not with a single movement, but we react at least with one-half of our body.

These problems are very important for the whole problem of action. Very likely in the tonic reactions we deal with an action which is in connection with a very primitive type of perception and with changes of consciousness and of the vasovegetative system. The vestibular nerve is finally a part of the system, one of the most important ones. But still the tonus of the posture and righting reflexes is the same kind as the tonus we get by changes in the vestibular function. We know that seasickness results very likely, not only by reason of the irritation of the nervus vestibularis but also because of the complete change in postural attitudes. There is also another connection between the centers for tone, consciousness and the vegetative system. I have wondered why up to the present time no one has ever studied what goes on in a nauseated person. A person who is nauseated is in a special state of mind. There are vasomotor changes. But I do not believe that interprets completely what is going on in the psyche of a nauseated person. We have a close relation between the nauseating effect and consciousness as such. The pleasure we get from nicotine, in a strong cigar for instance, consists partly in the slightly nauseating effect which such a cigar may have. We have mentioned the close relation between the function of the vegetative centers and consciousness and of course also tonus. It is not correct to say that by the effort of vomiting we feel weak afterwards, but the weakness is probably coördinated with all the other changes in the vasovegetative system and based on changes in tonus. We consider the vestibularis as the part of the tonic system in which we can best study all these mechanisms, and here I might make a remark which is perhaps again of interest from a psychoanalytical point of view. If one examines subjects after turning in the turning chair, we are often told that their world is turning around or that they themselves are turning around. One would say this movement which is induced by the irritation of the vestibularis has not an absolute relation either to the person or to the outward world, but this movement is in-between. Or we can say, in dizziness, we have before us a primitive state of mind in which the differentiation between body and world is so incomplete that the movement can be either projected or appersonated. It is therefore of interest to study dreams of patients with organic lesions of the vestibular nerve. The patients Eisinger and I have examined were partly patients in whom a cholesteatoma had destroyed some of the semicircular canals. These patients very often dream that they are flying, but sometimes they dream also that they see an aeroplane flying. Sometimes they do not see an aeroplane but they see a railway running very fast. Sometimes the patients run very fast themselves. In this irritation of the nervus vestibularis as such, we find in some way a fusion between the outer world and their own body. Such a fusion is a characteristic of a very primitive state of mind. We know what an important part projection plays in dreams. But still the vestibularis increases the tendency to projection and provokes projections of movements.

In the following discussions we shall often speak of so-called eidetic pictures. Eidetic pictures occur when a person looks staringly at a picture and then closes his eyes. Some persons, especially persons who are adolescent, get a mental picture which is not quite an image but has some qualities of perception; it is in some way between an image and a real perception. It belongs to a more primitive type of mind. When a person in whom we can obtain an eidetic picture gets at the time an irritation of the nervus vestibularis, these pictures begin to move. Sometimes the movement starts in one object and then goes on to another object and the first object becomes quiet. It is as if the movement as such could be easily transferred from one part of the eidetic picture to the other. We can formulate this in a general way: By irritation of the nervus vestibularis we get the perception of a movement, but this movement can be easily transferred from one object to another, and from the subject to the object, and from object to subject. Or we can say that the irritation of the vestibularis provokes marked changes in tonus and marked changes in consciousness and with these changes in consciousness we find not only projections of movement but also a transfer of movements.

The perception of movements can also be transferred and projected. The laws of these transfers and projections are akin to the laws we have found about the transfers of induced tone. These are the same laws Freud has found also about the libido. Energy, movement (perceived or performed), libido, cannot be abolished. When it is hindered from coming out in one place it comes out in another place.

CHAPTER III

ON ENCEPHALITIS

Among the tonic phenomena to be observed in encephalitis the tonic deviation of the eyes deserves special interest. These patients feel as if they were completely changed and this change again has some similarities to the change we find in depersonalization (Stern, Stengel). The different muscles of the body have different relations to life. The eye muscles have an especially close relation to psychic life. The muscles of the head and of the neck as well as of the tongue are also muscles that have a closer relation to the psychic life and to the emotions than others. I might remind you in this connection that in many of the catatonics we find especially negativism of the neck muscles and negativism in the jaw, but I propose to speak about muscles that are in closer relation to psychic life than others are. The eye muscles are in a very close relation to the optic perceptions; they are also in a very close relation to the nervus vestibularis and we deal with another apparatus which reacts to psychic influence very easily. The eye muscle movements are also very important for our perception of space. E. R. Jaensch has shown especially that the perception of dimensions is very closely dependent on our attention on the one hand and on the movements of the eye muscles on the other hand. In hystericals we so very often find changes in the perception of space—objects seem to be very distant, very far, or they seem to come nearer and become larger and larger. In depersonalization, about which we have spoken so often, I find quite similar changes. These patients complain that all objects are very far from them and sometimes perceive that the objects are not so big as they have been and as in a case I have observed in the Phipps Clinic, they have the feeling that all objects have not three dimensions, but only two dimensions. The real world appears like a picture. One of my patients complained that sometimes he felt dizzy at the end of the psychoanalytic hour and during the hour had the feeling that space suddenly came nearer and went away again. When subjects stare at a point and by will do not move their eyes there comes a queer feeling of change in the world and in the personality.

With these observations about the eye muscles we come to a field where there are not only tonic innervations, but also other muscular impulses. In order to study the psychology and physiology of tonus as well as other innervations it is worth while to study the manifestations in postencephalitis cases. I shall begin with a discussion about tic. Tic has for a very long time been considered as a purely psychogenic disease. If one reads the famous book by Meige and Feindel one will find that there tic is the habit of an individual who has remained infantile, especially in his movements. These writers made a very important observation. Some of the tic patients have coprolalia. They feel compelled to utter profane words and sentences. In some tic cases the psychogenic origin seems to be quite clear. I have observed, for instance, a girl who felt deceived by her lover. Her lover was not satisfied with the money her father offered him as a dowry and refused to marry her. The father after that was ready to give more money and the young man came back to the girl, but now she was in doubt whether she should accept him and she developed in connection with that a tic which consisted in turning away her head. This tic lasted a very long time. We have here a rather clear example of psychogenic tic. But we have to ask, why did she express her feeling of unwillingness towards the boy in such a motor way? There has been perhaps something wrong in her motor system from the beginning and maybe the idea of Meige and Feindel that there is some infantilism in the individual is not so bad. Maybe there is some apparatus in the brain of these persons which works in a special way and gives from the beginning a peculiar feeling in the conveying out of movements. This feeling is on the one hand responsible for the choice of this special organ for the neurosis, on the other the neurotic tendency gets a greater influence from the inferior organ. That an organic lesion on the basis of encephalitis can provoke a tic, there cannot be any doubt to-day. The question is: What special apparatus of the brain is affected. Most of the German writers think that a lesion of the striopallidal-substantia nigra system provokes the tics. Wilson denies it strictly. We do not know the lesion which provokes the tic. Maybe a cortical lesion, too, is necessary. They are not uncommon in encephalitis. But the lesion of the striopallidal-substantia nigra system certainly plays an important part. There is no reason to think that the so-called functional tic has to do with other organs.

I shall report a case I have observed with Gerstmann. This postencephalitic patient had a tic which consisted of opening the mouth widely, a kind of terrible yawning. She remained with her mouth completely open and she could not by her will close her mouth, but as soon as one touched the skin near her mouth she was able to close it. I have observed this case from the acute stage of encephalitis; there cannot be any doubt that this patient is an organic case. The motor phenomenon can be influenced by a touch and I report here some observations of Wartenberg who also found that organic movements can be influenced by pressure, touch and by thermic stimulations. Touching has the same influence on purely functional tics.

I might add some other observations. I once observed a patient with a so-called apraxia of the eyelids. The apraxia of the eyelids is an interesting phenomenon. These are patients who have the possibility of closing their eyes in a reflective way, but they are absolutely unable to close their eyes at a given command. Very likely in these cases we have to do with a lesion of the frontal lobe. When I touched the skin near her eyes she was able to close her eyes, but she was unable to if I did not touch her. The patient came to autopsy and there was an encephalitis periaxialis diffusa which affected especially the frontal lobe. Here there is no doubt that we deal with a purely " organic " symptom.

I have seen since choreic cases with this apraxia of closing the eyes. This apraxia could also be changed by touch. One of the best methods of treating organic or functional tics consists in the method of ordering the patient to exercise before a mirror and to touch at the same time with his finger the affected muscles. We see that the laws for the organic and the psychogenic tic are the same. We know that when we have a psychogenic tic and we cut the muscles which contract, a procedure which is sometimes made use of, another tic may appear in another part of the body. The same transformation can be observed in organic cases in a very clear way. I have observed a postencephalitic patient with blepharospasm who was treated by hypnosis prepared by medicine. The blepharospasm disappeared but instead of the tic there very soon came a tendency to look downward. The tic had gone from one group to another group of muscles. In quite the same way anxiety wanders from one object to another object. Not only tic but also other hyperkinesias may wander from one to another muscle group. There are also other very interesting phenomena in tic cases. I have told you about coprolalia in cases of psychogenic tic. There are observations in the literature which point to the fact that in the organic tic cases also coprolalia may occur; for instance, there is a case of E. Straus. His was a patient in whom a tic remained after chorea minor in the region of the mouth and the tongue. The patient uttered peculiar sounds with his lips. Often he felt compelled to speak about obscene things. Other observations of this kind can be found in the literature. This is a very important fact. E. Straus thinks that the coprolalia is certainly not purely psychogenic but has its foundation in articulatory, phonatory and respiratory hyperkinesis.

I may here mention an observation I made in Bloomingdale Hospital (White Plains):

L. Sc. Sixty years old; lawyer. Family history without interest. Had a psychosis twenty years ago. In 1926 his sleep and appetite became reduced. He felt persecuted by detectives. He would not want to eat " on stolen money." At first he was stuporous and rigid but by and by began to become clear and shows (February 29) the following picture: He moves continually and is hard to stop when speaking. He shows very marked stammering, very often at the end of sentences, but sometimes he makes snoring noises, and when he is listening his whole body is in movement. He clenches his fists, dovetails his fingers; makes little steps even when sitting. Sometimes he moves his feet at his ankles. He complains chiefly that the other patients tell him that he has a whore house; that his wife is a prostitute; that he practices fellatio. His movements increase when he speaks about his voices. He feels that he has to attack the people who treat him in such a manner. He has no other associated movements. Even when he does not speak he makes snoring noises, sometimes seemingly in connection with an impulse to speak. He has indeed often attacked other patients. He chooses mostly stronger and brutal ones who when attacked by him beat him up, so that he gets badly bruised when he attacks other people.

As the stammering and the tic have developed during the psychosis, one has a right to suppose that they are in connection with a lesion of the striopallidal system. Also his increased impulse to speech is in very close relation with this lesion. With increased impulses concerning speech the muscles of the mouth bring with themselves specific psychic contents. In the observation of E. Straus the striopallidal impulse provoked blasphemic tendencies. In this case tendencies are repressed and return by way of voices. This tendency of attacking people from where the voices come is very likely related to his increased motor impulses. These increased motor impulses increase his fighting instincts and very likely also his sadomasochistic tendencies. Brought up in a very severe way he does not allow himself to speak in a provoking way or to attack other people;

he is over polite in the psychosis, sadomasochistic and profane tendencies are satisfied in a roundabout way. We have a motor impulse of a special type and hyperactive motor impulses and these bring with them some aggressive tendencies. Straus' patient sometimes spits at the physician. These subcortical motor impulses are also closely related to special psychic contents. These organic hyperactivities increase the other activities, such as the aggressiveness and the destructive tendencies. We know this phenomenon to occur in post-encephalitic behavior disorders of children. They tear everything that comes into their hands, and destroy what they get; they are sadistic in a subcortical way. This idea that a motor impulse has its special psychic expression is of very great importance. Every hyperactivity, every great muscle strain carries with it a great amount of sadism. In the epileptic fit we find a great hyperactivity of the muscles, some tonic tensions. I am inclined to believe that there exists also some relation between the hyperactivity of the epileptic fit and the sadism which is so common in the epileptics. We come to the general idea that special psychic contents carry with them psychic motor impulses and that special motor impulses carry with them special psychic pictures.

Some other instances concerning motor troubles in encephalitis are of psychological interest. I have seen an acute case of encephalitis together with Gerstmann which had a hyperactivity of a more primitive type. The patient made rhythmic movements of flexion and extension at the knee and hip but when I prevented him from doing so by pressing down his leg, he began turning his leg inward and outward at the hip. The primitive hyperactivity could be shifted over from the flexors and extensors of the knee to the rotatory muscles of the hip. I have observed a patient with a horizintal nystagmus. The patient had at the same time a vertical nystagmus, but the vertical and horizontal nystagmus did not mix. When a horizontal nystagmus was present the vertical nystagmus could not appear. When the vertical nystagmus appeared, the horizontal nystagmus disappeared. We have to do with general laws of switching over of the energy from one part to other parts. We have already met this law of switching over in the induced tonus and the righting reflexes, and I may add also in the spinal preparations according to the experiment of Magnus we find the same law. The same irritation of the spinal preparation provokes either an extension or a flexion according to the position of the leg. From a general point of view we can also say that all the motor activities we have met in our discussions can be switched over. They have not a fixed relation to special muscles but there is energy and according to the psychic, or the organic switch, this energy is shifted over to one or to another group of muscles. This is the same law we found about anxiety and is the same law we meet in psychoanalysis so often, when we speak about the amount of libido which is given to one representation or is transferred from one representation to another.

We have considered the motor phenomena of encephalitis cases, but we do not meet with motor phenomena alone in the postencephalitic cases. There are some very interesting cases in which we meet with obsessions and many observations of that type have been reported. It is possible that these obsessions are again in connection with these motor impulses about which we have spoken and we might say that very likely, from a psychoanalytic point of view, they may be considered as impulses. I personally do not believe that an obsession is a pure representation or a pure idea which impresses the mind. Every obsession has once been a motor impulse and compulsion and only by repression has the compulsion become an obsession. All these postencephalitic cases have had these hyperactivity impulses and by repression of the motor component the impulse has become an obsession.

We know of many types of hyperactivity. Some patients increase the speed of their speech, they speak quicker and quicker. I may remind you that when we quarrel we begin to speak faster and faster. Between the increased psychic activity in the quarrel and the speed of the motor impulses there is a very close relation.

The so-called palilalia in encephalitis has to do with increased motor impulses on an organic basis. The problems of stammering are very closely related. We find similar mechanisms in stammerers very often. In a stammerer I have treated there was a great feeling of inferiority in connection with violent outbursts of his brother who spanked him very often. He tried to overcompensate it by special care in speech. He wanted to speak as exactly as possible. He tried to give answers very quickly and he developed too quick a tempo in his speech. Wanting to speak before the word was formulated he uttered inarticulate sounds, the words coming out in an incomplete way. He was not satisfied and was compelled to repeat. He spoke in very complicated sentences. He often made use of little words as namely, for instance, *exempli gratia,* in order to fill the pauses in the rapid speech. By regulating (diminishing) the speed of his speech, discussing his problems, he was cured in about a fortnight. Of course the real psychoanalytic problems as such lie much deeper. The discussion hinted at a special relation to his father. In such a case the increased impulses of speech are in connection with individual life problems. In postencephalitic cases the excess of energy comes from the wrong shifting over of the organic energy and impulse (antrieb). But these postencephalitic patients stammer also. Others speak in too loud a voice, others feel compelled to shout. Mostly the speed also increases during such a shouting attack. But there are some other possibilities of interpretation in the postencephalitic cases.

One postencephalitic patient with obsessions I have observed showed a remarkable increase in weight. The patient gained about thirty kilos in a short time. If we study a special group of postencephalitic psychoses we meet rather often changes in the metabolism and an increased weight.

I may report in this connection an extremely interesting case. The patient had a lethargic encephalitis when she was seventeen years old. She had also had troubles in her eye muscles. When I saw the twenty-two years old patient, she complained that she was very fat. She had come into the clinic because of paraphrenic ideas. Her mother and brother desired to abuse her in a sexual way. The brother came in himself during the night and brought other persons who also abused her sexually. She got very excited especially during the night and therefore came to the clinic. In the clinic during the day the patient was almost quiet; she had rather good insight into her psychosis and spoke about all her emotions in a way that indicated insight, saying: " I have had the delusion that people came in my room." When the evening came the patient became very anxious, and the anxiety occurred only in the evening, and at this time she wanted to have somebody around her. If somebody came to her the anxiety disappeared completely, but when left alone she began immediately to have hallucinations and paraphrenic ideas. The patient developed the idea that rats were coming into her room during the night and these rats bit her on the body and bit off her clitoris. She got very excited in connection with these ideas. The patient had had many sex experiences, but she was anesthetic. Her menstruation was not quite normal. The only way in which she got satisfaction was by cunnilingus.

She was given rather high doses of veronal and when the function of sleep was regulated all these phenomena disappeared. She showed then only the well known changes of the juvenile postencephalitic cases. She was rather forward, followed the physician during his rounds and got into quarrels with other patients. The delusions dis-appeared completely.

We can say from a purely psychological point of view that the patient had a regression and left the heterosexual level and adopted some perverted types of sexuality. Abnormalities in menstruation as well as troubles in her weight point to the diencephalon as the origin of these troubles. Again we find anxiety in connection with the sleep function and sex problems. The close connection between anxiety and sex is from the neurological point of view due to the common localization in the diencephalon. We find in this case in a rather striking way what is well known in neurosis, especially of children, that anxiety appears when there is no possibility of transference.

In other chronic encephalitis patients we meet also with states of anxiety on a purely organic basis in connection with lesions of the diencephalon. We infer that conversion in neurotic cases changes the function of the diencephalon.

But let us go back to the problem of motility. This motility of postencephalitic children and of the tic patients, as well as muscle tone, stands in very close relation to the emotions and the affective life. It is true as well for the tone of the righting reflexes, as for tone which is in connection with sleep and awaking (cf. narcolepsy). But to primitive motility there belong also automatic and rhythmic tendencies. They have some relation to the striopallidal system also. Besides these rhythmic tendencies are in close relation to the system of emotions and the affective life. We may say that, in general, the primitive, the instinctive motility has very close relation to the medulla oblongata, brainstem and the striopallidal system. Of course we should not forget that there is no motility which is isolated, the tone is also under strong cortical influence (I may mention the fronto- and temporo-pontine system). Also the nucleus ruber has many direct connections with the cortex. Then there are the primitive actions which come out in the grasping reflex and in the sucking reflex. The tendency to be observed in every suckling is to take every object and to put it into its mouth. They are to be observed in adults with special lesions of the cortical lobes (grasping reflex espe-cially after frontal lesions, but very likely also after striopallidal lesions, the sucking reflex in general paresis and in some cases of supramarginal lesions with apraxia of the face.) They are in con-nection with a freed subcortical action.

We can say that all these motilities are closely connected with the instinctive life. They belong, psychoanalytically speaking, to the " Id." Deliberate action, motility in which the pyramidal tracts play the leading part, that which makes use of all our perceptions and thoughts derived from perceptions, has a much closer connection with the cortical region. Of course it is not as if the cortex alone would then act. On the contrary, without the help of the subcortical structures no action is possible but the cortex is the leader and causes the melody of the action. This is the motility of the " Ego " in the psychoanalytic sense. (I myself prefer to speak about the " Perception-Ego ").

Meynert, the great Viennese psychiatrist, who is one of the founders of brain anatomy, made a section of the brainstem and demonstrated that all the higher activities are in connection with the basis of the brainstem, whereas the tegmentum, the dorsal part of the brainstem, contains the tracts for the more instinctive activities. Both systems have an influence on the spinal cord. He spoke about the double origin of the spinal cord from the brain. This conception certainly contains much truth.

I wish to comment further concerning the more primitive types of motility. One of the most primitive types of motor action is grasping. We know that the suckling has very well developed grasping reflexes, and we know that this can also be observed in frontal lobe lesions and in our encephalitic individuals with lesions of the striopallidal system. The grasping reflex is very closely related to the sucking reflex. They are often observed in the same case. I personally am of the opinion that sucking and taking of objects into the mouth is at least as primitive as grasping, especially if we consider these things from the phylogenetic point of view. Taking something into one's hand is in some way a symbolic action of taking something into one's mouth. It is interesting that if one closes one's fist one begins to sweat and this sweating, melting the objects, has very likely something to do with these tendencies of taking an object into the body.

This is a general idea which might help us in the interpretation of the fact that in organic cases in which we find snap reflexes we find also a grasping reflex (Schuster and Pineas). In one of the cases Dr. Freeman has observed there was also to be seen the snap reflex—as well as the grasping reflex. These very primitive functions are in some way basic for the motility of the Ego and have still some relation to the deeper parts of the brain and therefore I consider what I have told you about the motility of the Id and of the Ego as schematic. We have in the grasping reflex a very primitive action which is at the base of all our later action. There exists a very close relation between pictures, images, perceptions, representations and motor action. Every impression causes us to act in the direction of it. Even connotations change our condition. Every impression (picture, thought) induces us to make an action of grasping. Such grasping we find in all the cases of delirium tremens. The patient grasps whatever he hallucinates.

I have seen a patient with cerebral syphilis. This patient hallucinated always when attention was drawn in a special direction and one could in a suggestive way always provoke hallucinations. Whenever she hallucinated she at once began to grasp after her hallucinations. We can say that we find this tendency to grasping very clearly shown in all patients who have amnesic aphasia and who do not find the words for special objects. If they have difficulties they try to take their objects into their hands and the more primitive tendency of grasping comes out. But still the tonic tendencies are on a deeper level than the tendency of grasping.

Let us try to get a general scheme of motility. Whenever something appears in our world, we get at first " unconscious " perceptions of a primitive type. These perceptions, as we shall hear later, develop by and by. To the perceptions we react at different levels. There are at first these tonic tendencies by which we try to come nearer to the object (about which I have spoken in connection with the righting reflexes). In these tonic tendencies usually one-half or the whole of the body reacts. On the basis of these tonic tendencies the grasping sets in, the grasping goes on in different levels, too. We deal with the more primitive action of the so-called grasping reflex, then we have to do with the grasping reflex of the type of delirium tremens and finally with the grasping of deliberate action. But we find another important type of primitive action. When one is bowling he imitates the course of the ball by twisting his body in a tonic way. This is a primitive action by " tonic " or " clonic " imitation. This action by imitation has a magic background but coördinates also the individual to the actions of other individuals. Certainly this magic action by imitation belongs to the Id.

When, as we have stated, every action begins in a tonic way, we may say that every motor activity begins with the action of the apparatus which lies in the posterior part of the brain, and goes from there to the more proximal parts of the brain. Of course that again is schematic. Very likely the most primitive actions of the human being involve the cortical region also. But the focus of the figure of motility lies more in the posterior parts of the brain. When action develops the focus wanders more to the proximal parts of the brain. Of course this again is somewhat schematic. This conception is of some importance in connection with the fact that in the phylogenetic development of the brain, according to Monakow and others, function wanders from the posterior to the anterior parts of the brain. Von Economo speaks of this as " telencephalization." I have emphasized that special motility brings with itself special mental pictures. I have spoken of the psychology of the tic, and I have discussed the motility in postencephalitic children, and I may add that according to Eisinger's and my investigations there exist typical vestibular dreams. Thus motility is not isolated from other parts of the psychic life.

In order to go more into psychological details I shall now describe a case of cortical encephalitis: I knew the patient a very long time before she had her cortical encephalitis. Following an angina she developed a slight sensory aphasia with subcortical symptoms, such as cerebellar troubles of equilibrium, nystagmus and a monocular polyopia. At the same time there were hallucinations of animals. Before she got her encephalitis, this patient was often in the clinic, being treated for psychogenic troubles which were in very close relation to her married life. She had had relations with her husband long before she married him. At that time her husband had been married to another woman and the patient always reproached herself because she had had such relations with a married man. These self-reproaches prevented her from having complete erotic satisfaction. Her husband was much older than she and she identified him with her father. As a child she had always been very fond of her father. The mother accused the father of having sex interest in some way in his children. There was always quarreling in the home of our patient and when she first came into the clinic, it was partly because of these quarrels at home and partly in connection with the fact that she felt very emotional about the difficulties in her relation to this man, who later became her husband. It is interesting that this patient responded to these difficulties with a psychogenic tic, which was partly similar to sighing and to turning the head away. When I saw the patient for the first time it was about ten or twelve years after this initial difficulty. The patient came into the clinic because her husband—she was married at that time—had begun to have sex relations with another girl and she had scolded and reproached this other girl. The girl threatened suicide and the patient became very depressed and self-reproachful. She said that if the girl should commit suicide she would kill herself too. Behind this of course were the self-reproaches she had had when having sex relations with her husband while he was married to another woman, and the fact that she had wished the death of the first wife of the husband. But there was something also which she did not speak about when she was at that time in the clinic. The patient had been castrated (one ovary was left), very likely because of a gonorrheal infection from her husband. She was sterile and she had heard other people whispering that this mistress of her husband was pregnant. That was the fact that caused her despair and brought out some death wishes against the girl— death wishes which finally led to the idea that she must commit suicide herself. She identified herself also with her mother, who always reproached her father for being unfaithful and very often made violent scenes in which she accused her husband. I spoke with this patient about these troubles and I was able to dismiss her in a rather good state of mind.

A year later she came into the clinic again with a depression. The husband had confessed at that time that he had real sex relations with that girl and so she again developed a depression. In this state of mind she got an angina and in connection with this angina the encephalitis of which I have spoken. At the time when the organic symptoms were present there were mental confusion and hallucinations of running dogs. Now she developed another stage of the psychosis in the first part of which she had very vivid optic pictures, but to all outward appearances she was in a state of stupor. In these optic pictures her childhood came back and especially the relation to her parents. Very likely this regression to childhood and the optic pictures had a close relationship to the subcortical lesion of the brain. The subcortical lesion of the brain, however, did not produce anything new. Her old problems only appeared in a more primitive way. In the second part of the psychosis she developed a hallucinatory picture, which again bore a very close relation to her life problems, especially her castration and the fear she had lost her womanhood by reason of the castration. It came back in an archaic way. She heard voices saying that rats and deer were in her feces. These voices would accuse her of masturbation. The animals represented for her the children she wanted. Afterwards she believed the animals were in her stomach and that these animals should be removed by an operation. Later on the patient spoke about children she had with others, and children which should be removed from her bowels and finally she ended with hallucinations that she had got a luetic infection. When she had almost completely recovered she complained that people spoke about her, saying she had pubic lice and the last idea she had was that she had a bad smell about her genitals.

One could see that when the organic disease was at its height there was rather a deep regression. The more the patient recovered from the organic toxic state, the more her complaints took on the neurotic color and were more in accordance with the ideas of her daily life. The patient finally recovered completely. During the entire psychosis nothing happened that was not in close relation with her previous life, but because of the organic lesion all her problems appeared of a very primitive type. The organic lesion allowed the primitive material to come out. There is no doubt that the psychosis was an organic psychosis and that all the problems of regression were in very close relation with the organic changes in our patient's nervous system. In such a case we can study very clearly the close relation between the brain lesion and the psychogenic factors. The brain lesion does not make new material appear. From the moment a brain lesion occurs we live our life at a more primitive level.

The difference between a psychogenic regression and one of an organic type is to be found in the following direction: in this case we cannot say that we can find out the reason for such a deep regression as the patient has had. In organic cases we do not find reasons why the regression takes place. In the psychogenic cases we not only know the material and the regression but we know also the motives for the regression and this is in my opinion the shortest formulation of the difference between organic regression and psychogenic regression. In all these organic cases of which we have spoken we find regression and all the material which comes out in the regression, but we do not know the motive which has caused the regression to take place. In the psychogenic cases we know why a person goes back and we can say that there is a motive which drives the individual away from the present reality. This motive in some way is repressed in organic disorders of the brain.

As I mentioned during the first phase of the disease when the organic neurological symptoms were present the patient had hallucinations of a dog running from one side to the other. In the beginning it was impossible to find out what this dog meant for the patient, but in a later development it came out very clearly that it meant something very sexual for this patient. This sexuality is only partly in connection with the genitals as such but partly with the anal tendencies—she complained that animals had been found in her feces. This anal component led to the idea that there were many rats in her feces. The rat is an anal animal as is the mouse. In the deeper layers of the psyche magic animals are not only representative of genitality but they are the form of expression of some cloacal tendencies. Here is an interpretation for the animals seen in delirium tremens also. Of course we cannot get the interpretation of animals in delirium tremens directly because these deeper layers are symbolizations of such a primitive type that we do not get direct associations. Whenever an organic structure is destroyed we cannot know directly what psychic material is in connection with these deeper structures, but in an indirect way the material will come out; and from this material we can draw the conclusion that the deep structure also, as for instance the structure the lesion of which provokes delirium tremens, has connection with this sex material. We may never find out what the events in the fetal life are that make the points of fixation of the schizophrenic. We have as yet no access to the psychic events of the embryonic life. But we shall find very primitive material at higher levels in special arrangements and from this primitive material we can draw conclusions of what might go on in these deeper layers of thought.

One of the interesting hallucinations of our patient in the first part of the second stage of the psychosis was that her brother was in the house and that the house was burning. One of her brothers was indeed a chimney sweeper. It came out that this brother had had sexual relations with her when she was young, and very likely this burning of the house is a very primitive symbol for her sex tendency and her fear that she might be ruined by her sex relations with her brother. It did not come out in phantasies, at is would in a neurosis, but it appeared only in a delirious hallucination.

One of the important factors in the genesis of her psychosis was the fact that she had been partly castrated and was unable to have children. In her psychosis all these animals were not only symbolizations of anal-genital wishes but they were also symbolizations of children. At first she was in fear that the rats and the deer would be found in her excretions and finally she ended with the idea that she had children in her abdomen and the children would be taken out by operation.

If we study such a psychosis from the beginning we may find the same content at first in a very primitive way and later the same content becomes more and more adapted to the necessities of logical life because it becomes more and more subjected to rationalization. We can therefore draw the conclusion that where we cannot follow directly with our psychological understanding there will be a layer which very likely means something similar on a very primitive level. The hallucination of a dog running around in the very first phase when she had her nystagmus—contains very likely all these things which were later developed in the second stage of the psychosis. That she sees animals run in the phase of nystagmus is again not due to chance. The nystagmus produces moving hallucinations and when there are moving objects hallucinated, they are mostly living. What is going on in a psychosis organically is reflected in the psychic life and by the specific way of reflection of the organic in the psychic we can draw a conclusion as to what the deeper organic layers may mean psychically. These general remarks are also important for the psychology of dementia precox.

CHAPTER IV

ON OPTIC AGNOSIA

We shall try now to give a general view of what goes on in cortical lesions. I shall start with a discussion of lesions of the occipital lobe. There exists a case of mind-blindness described by Charcot. He reported a case where a man suddenly lost the possibility of representing something in an optic way. Charcot believed that the patient had lost all his optic imagination and that his orientation was impaired by the loss of optic images. No other function was impaired. But the patient complained that he felt in some way changed and also that he was not well oriented as to time. This picture is in so many ways similar to pictures that we may find in neuropathic cases, in cases of depersonalization, for instance, that Janet had the suspicion that this case might be a " scrupulent," and Freud, who had an opportunity of speaking with this patient, also got the impression that this man might have been a neurotic case. It is also rather unclear whether Charcot's case was really organic. There exists, however, another case of Wilbrandt, a case in which an autopsy took place, and this autopsy revealed serious lesions in the occipital lobe. This patient had the same symptomatology. She complained that she did not have vivid imaginations and that she could not remember anything in connection with the optic sphere. She also complained that time was in some way changed. She also had some hypochrondriacal trends, exactly the picture we meet in depersonalization. But in this case we do not have a right to say it was a neurosis. This case must have been an organic case. We come again to the fact that in this field also the neurotic and the organic troubles cannot be so different.

Let us now consider what such a psychic trouble really means. We are able to analyse depersonalization cases, and such analysis shows that such patients never lose their optic images. They complain and say: " I can't imagine anything any more," but if asked to describe the optic images, they describe them so very well and with so many details that one can be sure they must have optic images. They have them but they suppress them and defend themselves against them and there is always a motive behind this suppression. They do not want to know anything about their optic imaginations.

This is especially clear in depersonalization especially if it begins with the optic loss of the image of a special person. These things are very common in neurosis. For example I observed an obsessional neurosis patient who had an immense hatred against her relatives. She could not imagine the faces of these relatives, as in a case of a French writer. In a case of H. Hartmann's the depersonalization began in this way: The man was imprisoned as a thief and in the meantime his wife began sex relations with a peasant. The patient now in prison used to imagine the sex scenes going on between the two and had very vivid optic pictures, but suddenly he could not imagine it any more and following that he lost all his imaginations and then he complained chiefly, " I don't have any optic imaginations. I can't imagine anything any more." All the depersonalization, all the impossibility of getting an optic image, which is satisfying for the individual—this impossibility began with one situation and spread from this one situation, a law which is very well known concerning inhibition and anxiety neurosis cases. We know that anxiety mostly begins with a special situation and the anxiety spreads from this situation to similar situations or to situations in some way connected with the primary situation. Every repression has the tendency of spreading to more and more material. This is of very great interest for the genesis of the neurosis and also for psychoanalytic therapy. We know that whenever we succeed in freeing the patient from one repression at the same time he loses many other repressions. With the disappearance of one important repression many other repressions go at the same time.

In organic cases we find quite the same thing. I have observed a patient, for instance, who had an apraxia, especially appearing when writing or when trying to write. At the very moment he had this difficulty his organic difficulty spread and he became actually agnostic. He did not even realize that he had a pencil in his hand and lost it without perceiving it. There was an additional loss of function. Pötzl has pointed to these facts also. In one of these cases the organic narrowing of the visual field was increased when the patient wrote, a function which was impaired in him. In a case of slight sensory aphasia the understanding of words sinks to a deeper level when the patient gets an order in a field where he is dyspractic. Pötzl is right in supposing that here there is a general law.

But let us go back to depersonalization. We find that difficulties in optic phantasy and imagination occur if there is a tendency against these optic images. If we do not get full satisfaction by the process of representing; if we do not live fully in it, then we feel as if the representation did not exist. Similar symptoms as I have stated can be observed in many neurotic cases, but in some cases the brain lesion as such prevents us from living fully in our optic representation. What in the one case is produced by a motive, by a tendency of not knowing about a special fact, is in the other case caused by the brain lesion, or a brain lesion in this type of mind-blindness prevents living with full intention in one's own optic images.

But there are other very interesting types of optic troubles. If I show such a patient with mind-blindness optic pictures, the picture of a landscape with a church or some houses, some sky and some green fields, for instance, and then ask such a patient, " What do you see? "—then it will very often happen that such a patient sees, for instance, the church tower, but he will not see the church tower in its right place. Perhaps he will see the church tower very far away from the other part of the church. He might see the church tower in the air. If I ask, " Where do you see the green color? " he will see the green color but in the wrong place. This optic agnostic patient cuts his picture to pieces and mixes these pieces together. There will not be a loss of optic perception, but the single parts of the optic perception are intermingled. It may also be that such a patient will see a church tower he has seen before instead of the church tower in the picture I show him. Or it may be that I have shown him some flowers before and that one of these flowers will appear suddenly in the present picture. Pötzl, for instance, has shown a patient with optic agnosia a bunch of flowers, and the patient saw later one of these flowers instead of the tie of another person. What should be the remembrance appears suddenly as a part of the optic picture. We can also say that in these types of optic agnosia the single parts are present but not in the right order, and we see often that the different parts are intermixed. We find all types of condensation. We can also say that there is not only condensation, but we see that the relation in space can be completely changed. The patient may see the church tower with its point on the ground and the base in the air.

There is a very close relation between these pictures of perception of the agnostics and the pictures of a dream, but before I go into these I shall describe briefly the way in which those patients behave if one shows them some objects. I show such a patient the picture of a mouse. The patient will answer, " That is a cat." The next time I show the patient the picture of a violin and he will answer,

" That is a trumpet, or it is a fiddle." I show the patient a picture of a snake and he will say, " That is an animal." Or I show the picture of a candle and he will answer, " That is a match." I show him a ring and he will say, " It is a finger." Of extreme interest is the following reaction: If one shows the patient, let us say, a handkerchief, the patient will say, " That is *not* a handkerchief."

Let us consider what all these reactions mean. We can say: " Cat—mouse, those things which are very often associated with each other." But the mouse and cat both are animals. We might say that the patient takes instead of the picture which is present, something which is superordinated from a logical point of view. If the patient calls a violin a trumpet he takes something which is coördinated. But his perception is a perception out of the same logical sphere. It need not be the same logical sphere. It may be also the sphere of contiguity in space and in time. Between the finger and the ring, for instance, there exists contiguity in space. And we can say that in mindblindness the patient sees something which is logically related to what he sees, or he sees something which is related in space and time to what is demonstrated to him. In the last reaction of which I spoke, the patient has a complete negation for what he sees. If he says, " It is not a mouse," " It is not a fiddle," " It is not a match," he must have the real perception, but in some way he perceives in a negativistic way. All these kinds of perception every one of us has when he sees an object, not as the final phase of perception but as the beginning of the perception. It is very likely that whenever we see something we do not see in the beginning the definite, clear object, but we get at first a vague general impression of something which belongs in the group of furniture or something we have seen somewhere else in some other building. So by and by the impression develops from this vague general sphere to the more special impression; and very likely whenever such a development takes place one phase in this development is a phase where one gets the right impression, but doubts it again. We see quite similar things also when we begin to remember something— before the last positive synthesis, the last positive perception, comes, there is a negative phase, and this negative phase plays a very important part not in our agnostics only, but also in every psychic process. We can now formulate this in a more general way: The agnostic sees something every one of us might see before he gets the full perception. Or we would formulate it that the agnostic has an undeveloped perception, or to put it in another way, the perception of the agnostic remains in a vague general sphere and does not develop to a differentiated state of impression. These statements can be completed now by some experiments.

It is very interesting to study from this point of view the reactions of persons to whom some optic pictures are shown for a very short time (experiments by Pötzl, Allers and Theler). Many of those persons who see these optic pictures perceive only a very little part of them. For instance, we show them some picture made in Palestine where there are some Jews at the wailing wall. They see the wall and not the persons who are in the picture, but when they begin to dream the unperceived part of the picture comes back in the dream. All these things which have not come to full perception continue to have an influence. They appear then in a more or less clear way in the dream. Of course this is condensed with all the personal material, but we can see clearly that there has been a perception which has not come to consciousness. All this material will go into the dream and will appear there, not in a differentiated but in an undifferentiated way. Thus it is possible that this material undergoes the changes we meet so often in dreams, *i.e.*, condensation and symbolization. These experiments are very important because they show that something which is apparently not perceived is really perceived but in a very primitive way; and this very primitive way is a way which makes it possible to condense, to transfer one detail to another place. And all these unperceived perceptions, so to speak, follow the laws we know for dreams, the laws which we call with one short word the " Primärvorgang " (Freud), the primary action of the unconscious. We can also say that every perception before it comes to full consciousness passes through a phase which is an unconscious phase, in which the elements of the perception are combined quite in the same way as the single impressions are combined in a dream. Or every perception begins in an unconscious way and develops from the unconscious to the conscious. There is a general development which consists in a better differentiation and in getting a better order, and we can study it in every normal person. Similar experiments have also been made by Allers and Theler. Pictures have been shown for a very short time to the subjects. They perceived only a part of these. In associations, the seemingly non-perceived parts came up, but sometimes in a changed way. For instance, if the picture of a house with a ladder has been shown, the ladder has not been perceived but the ladder came out in the following association. It does not appear at the place where it should be but at another place or is mixed with some color which does not belong to it. We come to the general idea that the agnosia may be an unfinished perception and all of us before we perceive in the right way perceive in the same way that an agnostic person does.

We have another possible way of studying these problems, and this is the possibility of studying the eidetic pictures of E. Jaensch and Urbantschitsch, about which I have already spoken. If we try to get the optic images in ourselves we cannot keep these optic images steady. They change very often and if we study them we see that the color wanders from one image to another. One can study these things much better if one studies not optic images, but eidetic pictures. Eidetic pictures are psychic elements between optic representations and real perceptions. One obtains them if one shows juvenile persons or persons who have retained their juvenile faculty, some complicated picture, maybe children playing. The children may have clothes of different colors, or there may be a duck in the foreground, or one child may have a yellow hat. Then when the person has looked at this picture for a while we request the person to close his eyes and ask him what he sees. Maybe the person sees something but the yellow hat may not be on the head of the child where it has been, but on another child. In other words, the hat has been transferred from one place to another. Or if one of the children has blue clothes maybe the hat will now appear in a blue color and not in a yellow color. Or maybe two children are combined into one. Or we can say that in these optic eidetic pictures we have ourselves quite similar perceptions to those an agnostic person has. It is very interesting to study these eidetic pictures in psychoanalysis. Sometimes one gets patients who have optic pictures of this kind, and it is then possible to analyze these pictures in a very clear way. I refer to one instance concerning a man who was interested in painting and had very vivid optic imaginations. Once during psychoanalysis this man suddenly saw a hat and this was the only thing he had in his eidetic picture. Then I asked him for associations; there came out in association to the hat, the remembrance of a little friend he had when he was a boy, and that this little girl got crazy afterwards, and the patient himself was always in fear lest he might lose his mind. This eidetic picture represented his fear of insanity and expressed his emotions. We can see that a mechanism of the unconscious discovered by Freud has come out in this eidetic picture. Most of our spontaneous eidetic pictures are to be considered from a similar point of view. In quite a similar way a patient who had an optic agnosia, would see nothing but a hat. These eidetic images or pictures have the closest relation to what we could call the agnostic type of seeing.

But there is another relation which is not less important. That is the relation to vision in the peripheral visual field. It is very well known that perception in the peripheral parts of the visual field is not the same as perception in the central part of the visual field. If one examines the matter carefully one comes to the conclusion that perception in the periphery of the visual field is the same perception as in the agnostic cases. One cannot bring all these parts of perceptions into the right order. The nearer one comes to the central point of the visual field, the more the agnostic impression disappears and gives room to a clearer perception, to a better differentiated perception.

But let us ask what these facts might mean. We come to the conclusion that whenever we get an object into our visual field we do not get it immediately at the spot where we see it best. All our perceptions start in the peripheral part of the visual field and by and by go to the center of the visual field. Or we can say that every perception begins in an agnostic way and by and by an optic perception becomes a clear perception where everything is in the right place. There is the general statement that our perceptions in the beginning are agnostic. Or if you want to put it in another way, our perceptions in the beginning follow the laws of the unconscious and by and by come out of the unconscious to the better differentiation of conscious perception. (The system consciousness—perception of psychoanalysis. Pcpt. of Freud.) The perceptions are agnostic in the periphery of the visual field and they are also so if I expose a picture only a very short time to vision.

But all these ideas are still incomplete. We have to complete them by making the remark that children very likely have a perception which is much nearer to agnostic perception than our perception is. I told you that the optic agnostic object may be seen turned around its sagittal or longitudinal axis. W. Stern has found that children do not care very much whether one shows them a picture in a normal or an abnormal position. Whether we show children of a certain age the picture of a horse, standing on its head upside down, or upright, is of no importance for the child. We come also to the general conclusion that agnostic perception is a perception of a more childish type, of an unconscious type, and is also to be compared with the early phase of development of optic impressions.

We may continue with other facts concerning optic perception. Katz has made a differentiation between surface colors (Ober-

flächenfarbe) and space and plane colors (Raum und Flächenfarbe). Colors in space are those colors we see if we look into the
blue sky, like smoke or mist. We know that some objects have
similar colors. When we look, for instance, into a corner of a dark
room, the color does not adhere to the surface of the walls, it is spread
over it (plane color). It is interesting if we compare these space
colors with the colors that are closely connected with the surface.
Objects, for instance, such as a chair, have a special color and its
color is in special relation to the other parts of the object. In some
way it is immediately on the surface. We have reason to believe that
the surface colors are the more developed colors and the space colors
are the more primitive colors. When congenitally blind people get
vision by operation, they see space colors. The color is spread on
the whole room or it lies at least over the surface of the objects.
Gelb has found in occipital lesions that the patients have lost the
possibility of seeing surface colors. The colors are not in close relation with the object but envelop the object and the finger dives into
the color, which is in some way around the object. We have a new
example for the general law, that with a brain lesion the more primitive type of perception comes back which is at the same time also the
type of perception which belongs to an earlier stage of development.
We come therefore again to the general conclusion that the brain
helps us to develop our undeveloped psychic material, or, in other
words, lesions of the brain cause the development of the perception to be arrested before it should be.

What I have said here about the agnosias in the optic field is not
only true concerning agnosias of every type, but it is also true for
disturbances of speech. It is not true that the brain lesion destroys
any representations. Representation can never be entirely destroyed.
We are of the opinion that the brain lesion causes us either to be
unable to live fully in our perceptions, that is one type of mind-
blindness, or to be unable to develop our perceptions to the highest
level. The perceptions remain at a lower level.

How can we interpret this from the point of view of brain
pathology? The tendency in the older brain pathology was to believe
that the interruption of association fibers between the primary centers
of perceptions and between the centers of perceptions and representations causes the troubles. This theory is absolutely wrong. All these
lesions about which I speak are not lesions of association fibers but
these lesions are lesions of centers, and if there is a lesion of the
centers there is no longer the possibility of getting a full development

of the perceptions. But there is one instance in brain pathology which shows that the lesion of long fibers of medullary sheaths produces disorders of the group of "agnostic" troubles. After a lesion of the anterior and median part of the corpus callosum one finds that the left side of the patient is apractic. Such a patient is usually able to handle objects but he will usually not be able to make imitating or active movements when the object is not present. The more instinctive the action which is asked the better he can perform it. This is indeed a lesion which interrupts the connections between the left and the right center of praxia. It seems that the right center of praxia which does not show any lesion at all, cannot work alone in the way it should without the help of the left center. But it is interesting that so-called sympathetic apraxia of the left hand does not consist in that some movements are not possible or have disappeared completely, but the movement falls back to the more primitive type; only more instinctive movements are possible. One would say in this case that we have to differentiate these two centers. The left center is superior to the other and if the other center is compelled to act alone then we do not find the lack of special elements but we find a more primitive type of action. And we can also say that in the case of apraxia the center in the left hemisphere causes the action of the left hand to be developed to a higher degree; or we can say that the interruption of the so-called association fibers does not bring to pass that here are some elements not connected with the other, but that the subordinated center acts in a more primitive way. You see that here there is something quite similar to that which is seen in the loss in optic agnosia.

But here we come again to some rather important problems. Why do these patients act towards real objects better than to objects they only imagine? And here we come to a formulation Jackson made many years ago. He says that whenever we have a lesion of the cortical region the higher propositional act will be disturbed. What does he mean by "the higher propositional act"? We can say that whenever we have a lesion of the cortical brain that it will happen that all functions which are instinctive go on excellently, but what is intellectual and not in immediate connection with an important biological need will not go on well. The same is true about the speech troubles we shall discuss later. There is a difference between emotional speech and intellectual speech. Emotional speech is preserved when intellectual speech has undergone changes. Or suppose we have before us an apractic patient. The apractic patient when getting angry will have excellent gestures of anger. He will threaten you, perhaps, with his fist. But when his anger is gone and you say to him, " Please show me how to threaten somebody," he will not be able to. Or we can also say that the brain lesion makes the more intellectual action impossible whereas the emotional action is possible. We have the right to say that the emotional action is phylogenetically and ontogenetically prior to the intellectual action, or we can say this is also a type of regression. We can also say that in a general way a lesion of the cortical region will cause a regression to take place. There will come a type of perception which is more like the type of perception in the child. There will come a type of action which is more emotional. There will come a type of speech which is more like emotional speech. These more primitive functions are at the same time the way in which we begin our actions; the way in which we begin to speak; the way in which we begin to perceive. In every individual intellectual action, in every individual perception, there must have been a phase of a more primitive type, a phase of a more emotional type, and we can say in a general way that every one of our actions, every one of our perceptions, has a development from the primitive, from the phylogenetic, from the ontogenetic prior one to the more developed one. The ways of this phylogenetic old one are the more emotional ones and follow the laws which we know in psychoanalysis as the laws of the unconscious. Or, generally speaking, every lesion of the cortical optical region makes the process of perception go on in a more unconscious way with condensations and symbolizations and with changes in the sphere of perception insofar that in such a perception something is taken which is either subordinate, coördinated or superordinated in the logical sphere or something which is only in space or in time or in touch with what is really meant.

CHAPTER V

ON SPEECH DISTURBANCES

Speaking about language I shall begin with a most simple instance, *i.e.,* with that of slips of the tongue. It is not necessary for me to repeat what is known concerning the psychology of a slip of the tongue in daily life. We know that in every slip of the tongue of the normal and neurotic there is a tendency—a wish to express something that should remain hidden; something the person is interested in. There are also slips of the tongue to be observed so often in cases of slight aphasia, in cases of general paresis, in all kinds of aphasia, in the phases of restitution. These slips of the tongue are not only to be found in those words which are of importance to the individual. We can see here an important general law which is to the effect that when there is an organic lesion of the cortex, there is a lesion throughout, in every content; whereas in neurotic troubles very often the trouble is only to be found in those words and in those expressions which mean something special for the individual. That is indeed the difference between neurotic slips of the tongue and slips of the tongue of aphasics. I would like to say that the organic disorder manifests itself in psychic contents which are of no importance for the individual whereas the neurotic and the schizophrenic disorders occur in those words which are of importance for the individual. What is true for the slip of the tongue is true for every aphasia. In motor aphasia we find that the troubles do not occur in close relation to the affective value of the words. It is about the same with sensory aphasia: in sensory aphasia the troubles of understanding are present as well when I ask the patient something which is of great importance for him as when I ask something which is of no personal importance for him. Still emotions and affectivity play some part in every aphasic patient, but we can formulate the difference in the following way. In the non-organic troubles we have a motive for misunderstanding, whereas in the aphasic troubles we have no motive for not understanding. But still the organic troubles have all very much to do with the state of emotion in which the individual is. We know, for instance, that patients with motor aphasia show more marked troubles whenever

46

they get excited. The excitement has a much greater influence on the speech of a motor aphasic than it has on that of a normal person. But it is more the excitement as a whole which has an influence than the special contents. But pointing to the differences we should not overrate them. Every motor or sensorimotor trouble depends on the whole situation. In sensory aphasia the situation may help the patient to understand words and phrases he cannot understand under other circumstances. The motor aphasic sometimes finds words under emotion he could not find otherwise. Sometimes the difference between the normal and the aphasic consists only in the dependence of the aphasic on the special situation. He is not adaptable any more. He succeeds sometimes only if he is in a very concrete situation, he fails if the situation is of a more abstract type (*cf.* what I have said about apraxia). Goldstein has especially pointed to this fact.

Even complexes may influence aphasic troubles. The organic more general inhibition is therefore in its nucleus akin to the psychic—complex—inhibition. Also in the organic trouble the word is not lost. When the situation is fitting, either the articulation or the understanding will appear. Of special interest are the so-called paraphasias in sensory aphasia cases. If one studies carefully troubles in finding the correct word, one finds the following general aspects: if a patient should find the word " paper," it will happen very often that he does not find the whole word; he finds only a part of the word. He may say instead of paper " aper " or " per." But what did not come out in the first attempt may come out in the next one or spontaneously. Very often a part of the word which should come out is repressed but this very part of the word still lives and will come out later in another combination.

I once showed a patient with sensory aphasia the picture of a butterfly (Schmetterling), the patient called it Fledermaus (bat). The fact which is responsible for the choice of this word is that both words belong to the same logical sphere (flying animals) and the middle of the words is almost identical, *etter—eder*. . . . In the next attempt the patient called the picture Fletterling, condensing the two words. Finally she succeeded in finding the right word, "Schmetterling." In the same way in the dream material condensations take place. Finally she found the word " Fledermaus." Such a series follows the same direction as a chain of free associations in which finally the repressed material appears. We know in a chain of associations that the thing repressed comes out at first in condensations and symbolizations until it appears in the way it is in the unconscious. The best instances for all psychoanalytical laws of condensation, symbolization and transfer, can be found in the paraphasias of improving cases of sensory aphasia.

I add some examples taken from a case of Leitungsaphasia (aphasia of conduction). The patient had his chief troubles in repeating words and phrases. When he is asked to repeat the word (foliage) he says " It is out of doors." Instead of Löwe (lion) he repeats Wölfe (wolves) and Gölfe (meaningless). When he is asked to repeat (child), he repeats a child; instead of Monday (Montag) ; to-day (heute) (it was Friday).

We also find in paraphasic mistakes words of the same sphere— words akin in sound or in logical content. There are contaminations. Sometimes the intention of finding the right words succeeds after going through condensations. That is as well an analogy to what one finds in mind-blindness and what one finds in neuroses. Also what is repressed in the neurosis tries to come into consciousness and what is sent there becomes more and more similar to the repressed until the repressed is finally in consciousness. The language of children offers interesting analogies. I quote an observation by W. Stern that one child makes use of the word " peep-peep " for all things with wings; that is for butterflies, for insects, for birds, and we can say the child is not concerned much about the differentiation. There is a general connotation and word for all things that have wings. I remind you that the case I have mentioned called (Schmetterling) butterfly at first a (Fledermaus) bat. Stern's child calls a chest a bichu. In the drawer were her books (Bücher) with pictures, and she asked for the book with this word bichu. Afterwards all chests were " bichu," not only the chest in which the books were. She called also chests books, because once the books were in such a chest, books in which she had been interested. Here the choice of this special word has been made by " contiguity." We may see identical mistakes in aphasic patients. For instance an aphasic patient will very often call a watch, hand, and the hand, watch, and whenever there are two things often together, the aphasic patient will very often use the name of the one for the other. In another famous example of infantile language (Romanes), a child had learned when seeing the duck in the water the word " quack " and soon called all birds and all bird-like things " quack," finally also a coin on which was an eagle and also other coins on which there was no eagle at all. Finally she called all shining things " quack." This is also an example which we could duplicate as well in the neurotic case as we could in the case with an optic agnosia, but we would also find it in cases of sensory aphasia. It would be quite possible that a patient with sensory aphasia, when he is asked about a coin might call the coin a bird or would say " quack " to it. Of course we would not understand it because sometimes it is not so easy to discover the reasons for the mistakes of sensory aphasic patients, but if we examined them long enough we should find out that every paraphasia has some reason which is in connection with the previous psychic life. But these previous events which go into the unconsciousness are not so important as events of life which produce neurotic mistakes. Certainly when the patient calls the butterfly a bat, there must be something in her individual experience that helps her to make such a mistake. When a neurotic patient, however, makes such a mistake we would be suspicious and we would say, " What kind of experience did she have with a bat? " Maybe she has had the common fear that the bat might get into her hair or maybe it has been a symbol for her that she is afraid she will lose her virginity. That would be a possible interpretation for a neurotic case, but not so for the organic case. The speech troubles in the motor aphasia patients can be understood in a similar way. If a patient with a motor aphasia can pronounce the word " artillery," he will not say " artillery " but " arlitery." He has the possibility of pronouncing every sound but he cannot make use of his faculties. In motor aphasia we have the word sometimes cut into its single pieces and every single part is put into the wrong place. In sensory aphasia we find that the whole syllable is preserved but the syllables are in the wrong order or the whole sentence is cut into pieces and the single word is in the wrong order.

This leads to the very important problem of what is going on in ourselves when we utter a sentence. We are wrong if we believe that we formulate at first one word and then another and finally the last word of that sentence. That is not true. One has spoken about the general idea of sentences (Gesamtvorstellung). Every sentence is at first present in a very vague and general way as a germ. We have at first the tendency to sentences—the tendency is there before the first word has been spoken. There is some general direction. What I have stated about perception is also true about the sentence. The development is not so that the first word and the second word and the following word are prepared, but there is at first some vague general scheme of the sentence and the general scheme is developed and this development, these chaotic single words, get into their right places. When I say for instance: "Very likely snow will fall down," probably before I have begun the sentence, I have already had a vague notion that the word "down" will be here. The word "down" is in my Gesamtvorstellung (general idea) from the beginning. The first and the last word of the sentence are at the same time in consciousness but undeveloped. Very likely it is not only the single sentence which is prepared in such a way, but when we begin one sentence, we know already the words we shall make use of in the next sentence and we see very often that when someone speaks sometimes a word suddenly comes out which does not seem to fit at all into what he says. It is the word of the next sentence which is already prepared and developed too early. We must have a general scheme. Our general tendencies go far into the future. The Gesamtvorstellung is like the "latent thought" of a dream and we know that in dreams as in language condensation takes place and that during the development very often the words are cut into pieces and the pieces are in a seemingly mechanical way united with one another. The language of the dream is indeed very akin to the language of our aphasic patients and especially to the paraphasias of an aphasic patient. We can say that these troubles in the differentiation of the "Gesamtvorstellung," the general idea of the sentence, may be troubles concerning the syllables or sounds or they may be troubles in making use of the words, or, an especially interesting specimen of that kind, they may be troubles in the grammar. It is furthermore very interesting to see that there are types of aphasia, and very likely as well of motor as of sensory aphasia, in which the patients lose the faculty of speaking in a grammatical way, and of appreciating the grammar. These patients speak, as one might call it, in an agrammatical way. It is interesting that we find the same type of language in special phases of the development of the language of children and we find the same type of language in all languages in which gestures play a very important part. I might add in this connection that one finds sometimes similar things in schizophrenic patients. I have seen such a case in which the patient made use of this agrammatical language only when he spoke about things which were very important for him. The schizophrenic goes back to this archaic language when he wants to say something which has to do with his innermost personality. The motor aphasic will make use of this agrammatical language for whatever he wants to say.

I cannot go into the details of the language of schizophrenics. I refer to the paper Dr. White has written on this subject and would like to make use only of one instance he has given there. When the primitive man sees that a stag runs fast and some Indians run fast, he will have the feeling that some of the Indians might be stags or on the other hand that some of the stags might be Indians. Of course for the primitive man and for the schizophrenic this means not only the word but also the meaning. An aphasic in a similar condition might also call an Indian a stag, but generally he will not be really mistaken about it, but will only make the mistake in the word. In order to state it in another way, in aphasia and in the language of children we find the same troubles with the words that we find in the meanings and the connotations in schizophrenic patients and in primitives. Maybe the Indian will not kill the stag, believing that the stag might be a human being. A paraphasic patient who is a hunter will never be troubled in such a way by his aphasic trouble.

We come again to a very general conception. In aphasia, in agnosia and in organic troubles we find the same general trouble. It is the difficulty of taking one thing instead of subordinated, coördinated, superordinated things or instead of something which is related only in space or time to it. Condensation takes place. That is the general difficulty and I think that in the psychic life there does not exist any other disorder. That is the same trouble we find in dreams, in neurosis, and in schizophrenia. The general trouble is always the same, the difficulty of differentiation and the difficulty of integrating the raw materials or we have only one primary trouble in the psychic life, a trouble which is best described in the interpretation of dreams by Freud. Freud speaks about the Primärvorgang (the primary psychic action) and he states that the primary psychic reaction consists in the fact that we have symbolization, condensation, by the transfer of an amount of libido from one place to another, and timelessness and the difficulty in differentiating between inward and outward reality.

That is in brief really the sum of dream interpretation; of the one primary trouble which can take place in different parts of the psychic life. These different parts of the psychic life are the following ones. One part of the psychic life is the material which belongs to the nucleus of the personality and that is the material of the emotional life. This is the material which is disturbed in all neuroses, in schizophrenics, in dreams. This is the material which is in very close relation to the primitive functions of the brain which are localized around the cerebral ventriculi, *i.e.,* the parts of the brain which are phylogenetically older. We can say that in those parts of the brain the essence of life remains unchanged and does not take on a final shape. That is the part of the brain which belongs chiefly to what in psychoanalysis we call the " Id." In the so-called organic troubles we have spoken about we find the same " Primärvorgang." We find again, as I have told you, troubles in differentiation and in integration. The contents are cut to pieces and the pieces cannot be united in the right way. One piece is taken instead of the other one and the contiguity of space and time is sufficient to take the one thing instead of the other one. The primary trouble is the same, but the trouble is now not a trouble in a sphere which belongs to the nucleus of the personality, but there is trouble in the perceptions, in the words which mean something for us as well as those which do not mean very much for us. It is not the emotional part in the perceptions and words which is disturbed in these patients or if so only in a secondary way, but what is disturbed is the apparatus of the brain or something which is only a tool for the deeper psychic forces. There are troubles which are in the periphery of the personality and we can say these are the troubles of the " Ego " in the psychoanalytic terminology. In this " Ego " we find the same troubles, but only in material which is less important for us from the point of view of personality and more important for us from the point of view of a tool of the personality. This " perception ego " has less life in itself than the emotional " It."

That is a general idea about the psychic structure. In between these groups there are two other groups we have to consider and these are the groups in which we have troubles in the connotations, in the purely intellectual sphere, the trouble we find in the general paretic; these troubles are in many ways much more akin to the troubles of the ego sphere about which I have spoken and to the troubles of perception than to the other troubles. Indeed we find in all processes which end in dementia, in the common sense, very often at the same time troubles in the field of gnosia, praxia and speech. For instance in dementia senilis and in general paresis. There exists another sphere between the perception as such and the emotional part of the personality. This is the sphere which is troubled in the so-called states of mental confusion. The confusional states can be differentiated from the schizophrenic states in that we can say that in confusional states the personality is never so much

involved as in schizophrenic states. In schizophrenic cases there is
something which lies in the center of real driving forces, in the
center of the " Id," whereas in the confusional states the trouble lies
between the Id and the Ego, in those psychic layers which help to
work up the results of the perception of the Ego for the Id.

The general scheme is that we have in the psychic life different
layers, one layer is a layer of the Id which is in connection with
the phylogenetically old parts of the brain, an emotionally deeper
part of the personality, and then there follows a layer which is the
connection between the deeper part of the personality and the perceptions, a layer which is troubled in mental confusion. Then there
follows a layer which has to do with the perceptions and with
dementia and this is troubled in the cases of agnosia, aphasia and
organic troubles of cortical lesions. These layers are psychogeneti-
cally younger but they are more rigid and contain less life than
the layers of the *Id*. All these layers when there is an organic lesion
show the same primary change. They always show difficulty in
differentiation and integration. They always show such condensations as we see in the dream. Or we can say that every trouble puts
in the place of the mechanism of the waking state, the dream mechanism. In aphasia, however, the dream mechanism acts on the words,
whereas in the schizophrenic person the dream mechanism acts
on the important emotional nucleus of the personality. (That is, of
course, very schematic: In every aphasia, *e.g.,* connotations are also
impaired.)

I wish after this more general conception to go back to the agrammatic troubles which are of interest to us because we see so many
relations between the agrammatical troubles of brain lesion cases and
the agrammatical phases in the development of language in children
and the agrammatic structure in the most primitive language, that is
the language of gestures. We come back to our general ideas, that
wherever in one of the psychic layers a trouble takes place, there
we shall find a regression. The law of regression is not only true
about the Id, the law of regression is also true about the Perception-
Ego. We can also say that dream interpretation must help us to
understand the mechanism of organic troubles of the brain.

CHAPTER VI

THE POSTURAL MODEL OF THE BODY

After discussing these general ideas about disorders of speech I shall go now to a very important special problem of brain pathology. This is the problem of the so-called postural model of the body, or as we call it in Germany the " Körperschema," the scheme of the body. What does this expression mean? The expression means that we have in ourselves in some way a picture of what our own body may be. We have a postural scheme of our body in our psychic life in consciousness and in the unconscious. The postural scheme of the body comes out in a very clear way in those persons who have lost a limb suddenly. If a person loses his limbs by tuberculosis or by some other chronic disease, then as a rule the bodily scheme will not come into action, but if some one loses a leg by amputation, by trauma, by a bullet, he will mostly develop something which we call usually a phantoma, a phantoma of the hand or a phantoma of the leg. He has the feeling that the lost limbs are still present.

I have seen an invalid who was once sitting somewhere on a high chest and did not realize that he did not have his two legs and jumped down and hurt himself rather badly. These persons not only do not know that they do not have their legs but they feel positively that they have them. They feel it and many of them visualize their lost leg in a very vivid way. This is the phantoma. The phantoma very often preserves the last position in which such a patient has had the limb. (*cf. Riese.*) When a patient has lost his hands when he was shooting the phantoma preserves this position. Such a phantoma remains in such a position for many years. In one case in which there was such a phantoma it remained for fifty years. This phantoma retains a state of the body in which the body was intact or it is by self love that the individual continues to feel his limbs.

It has been believed that the phantoma is provoked by a peripheral irritation of the nerves. By injecting cocaine into the skin of the remaining part of the limb the phantoma may disappear. But certainly what is going on in the place of the amputation can never explain the phenomena of the phantoma. Some of these patients with phantoma feel that their toes are squeezed by too narrow shoes. This cannot be anything in connection with a peripheral lesion. It must have to do with the central picture a person has about his own body, *i.e.,* the postural scheme of the body. Some of the patients retain only the knowledge of the radial parts of their hands and arms. This may be in connection with the cortical representation of the hand. Some of these persons preserve the picture of their hand very well but it comes nearer and nearer to the shoulder until it reaches the point where the amputation took place. The hands are better preserved in the phantoma than the other parts of the arm. Instead of a hand in its natural shape very often after some time has passed a little hand appears and many of the patients speak about the hand as of the hand of a child.

All this shows that there are central processes going on in connection with narcissistic wishes. These insure that the patient feels the body as it has been before and especially those parts of the body which mean something for the individual. We know that, for instance, the erotic significance of the hand is much greater than the erotic significance of the forearm. It is also true that in this postural scheme those parts are much better preserved which are in connection with the external world. One of my patients felt in the phantoma only the toes and the heel and in between there was nothing at all. Something must go on in the central parts of the brain. Wishes and tendencies of the individual have something to do with the postural scheme of the body. Head observed the phantoma disappear after a parietal operation.

We come to the general point of view that the phantoma is an expression of the picture we all have in ourselves about our own body and this picture is in some way related to the narcissistic libido The individual does not acknowledge that his beloved limb is not his any longer. When amputated persons dream, they never know anything about the loss of their extremities. They walk around as if they had never lost their extremities and only after awaking do they become aware that they have lost them.

These are not the only facts which prove that we build in ourselves a picture of our own body, but there are many other facts which point in the same direction. I may begin with the report of some organic facts. When you examine a great number of cases of tabes it will happen very often that when you irritate one leg of the patient, the patient will not feel the irritation in that leg, but he will feel it in the other leg. We call this alloesthesia. When the transfer is absolutely symmetrical we speak of allochiria. Dusser de Barenne has obtained similar symptoms in animals. He has made special transections of the spinal cord and he could provoke all kinds of allochiria or alloesthesia varying with the distance between the two experimental transections of the spinal cord. By some spinal mechanism some relation is already made between the symmetrical parts of the body or in our bodily scheme very likely the symmetrical parts of the body are united partly by spinal, partly by medullary mechanisms. I myself have seen a parietal lesion with alloesthesia. Whenever I touched one side of the patient she felt not only the touch on this side, but she felt also a touch on the other side. Or in other words there is some organic connection between the symmetrical parts of the body and this connection is an organic connection built up at different levels and one of these levels is very likely the spinal cord and one is a level which belongs to the parietal lobe. We come thus very near to hysterical cases; the so-called allochiria about which Jones in his preanalytical days wrote an excellent study. In these patients we see sometimes that the left side of the body is projected towards the right side and the right side of the body is projected towards the left side. We know that there are cases with parieto-occipital lesions, who lose the possibility of building up a knowledge of their own body. They do not find their hand for instance. They are quite disoriented about their eyes and they are quite disoriented about their fingers. Unfortunately most of those cases which *Pick* has described are cases in which there are diffuse lesions of the brain, but certainly we deal with organic lesions of the brain which hinder us from getting a clear perception of our own body. There is a very important fact that in these purely organic cases, the patients are not only disoriented about their own body, but at the same time they cannot orient themselves about the body of other persons. But mostly the disorientation about the body of other persons is not so great as their disorientation about their own body.

Very likely all these cases are of a parietal type. Gerstmann made a special study of an agnosia concerning fingers, finger agnosia. There was difficulty concerning the choice between right and left and a difficulty concerning the knowledge about the fingers. We know that these cases are very often unable to distinguish one finger from another. They are absolutely unable to learn that that is the pointing finger or that is the ring finger and they make these mistakes no matter how often they have learned it. It is interesting that these persons get disoriented about the fingers of other persons. These cases have at the same time difficulties in writing and in the possibilities of reckoning. Very likely it has to do with the fact that primitive reckoning has something to do with the use of the fingers and these cases show how close the relation between the knowledge of the hands and the function of writing may be. We can also say that in this bodily scheme the fingers play a special part. The distinction between right and left in the bodily scheme can be disordered very easily because we learn rather late to distinguish between the right and the left side. Those who live in countries where people have to go into the army whether they want to or not, know that many boys learn with great difficulty the distinction between the right and the left side. And when they know it theoretically they are far from making use of it in their actions. It is interesting that in the experiments of Pawlow when he creates a conditional reflex on one spot of the right side, he very often gets a conditioned reflex from the symmetrical part of the other side. In other psychological experiments when, by special practice, a finer distinction of two spots has been obtained on one part of the body the symmetrical part would also show finer perceptions.

It is very easy to repress parts of the body scheme and this repression can be an organic repression and can also be a psychological repression. There are some cases in which the patients forget that they have two sides of the body; mostly they forget their left side, especially when there are some special troubles in the sensibility of the left side. This is related to the fact that most of the hysterical troubles of sensibility are on the left side of the body. If we analyze these organic cases there is shown a tendency of not being aware of a lesion of the body, something similar to what comes out in the phantoma. The phantoma is as we have stated in connection with a narcissistic wish to retain the whole of the body. Here the patients in some psychological organic way exclude that part of the body which does not give satisfaction. The organic lesion provokes something which is very similar to what we call in psychoanalysis a repression. It is mostly the left side of the bodily scheme which is excluded by organic lesions of very different kinds or by something going on in the so-called psychic sphere in hysteria.

There are some parts in the bodily scheme which have special importance, for instance, the middle line. It plays a very important part in organic cases. I have spoken chiefly about agnostic troubles in the bodily scheme, but there are also apractic troubles of the postural scheme. We know that some cases have an intact postural scheme, but they cannot make use of it in action; they are unable to point to their nose, and we find patients who do not show any other signs of apraxia but cannot point to special parts of the body. Some are able to point to their eye, but they are only able to point to their right eye with the right hand and are unable to point to the left eye with the right hand. It is as if in these patients there were a too well defined midline and as if this midline could not be passed by the individual. The midline of the head is different from the midline of the trunk and patients who are unable to cross the head midline are very well able to cross the midline of the trunk.

These problems are not only problems of organic neurology but also play a very important part in the neurosis. I remember a boy who had a latent obsessional neurosis. He always felt compelled to scratch himself in the midline of the head. He was very much impressed by a poem by Uhland which is taught in German schools, in which a Turkish soldier is cut in the midline by some German soldier, so that one half of the Turk falls to the right side and the other half falls to the left side. This patient at the same time felt a special disgust of all things which are parted in the midline, and he had a great anxiety concerning wounds, and of course especially concerning female genitals. From a psychoanalytic point of view the significance of the midline is partly in connection with the fact that the genitals are also in the midline. In organic lesions of the spinal cord we find very often that the genitals do not show disorders in sensibility whereas the skin around does. If neurotics have symptoms concerning the midline it has to do with things which are organic as well as psychic. I may remind you of the special importance of the midline in embryological development. In all animals that are symmetrically built we shall find special formations in the midline. In the midline are not only the genitals but also the mouth and anus. I wish only to emphasize the fact that these problems of postural model reach very far and are problems which are as well problems of organic neurology as problems of the structure of the whole body and problems of the psychoneuroses.

The postural model of the body is not the sum of optic kinesthetic and tactile sensations. It is an integration. It is still worth while mentioning that whenever in optic agnosia there is a serious damage of optic perceptions the postural scheme will be so affected that not even localization is possible without making quick little movements (Tastzuckungen) (Goldstein and Gelb). The tactile impression alone would give only a very primitive idea of the postural model. One can prove this point of view by a simple experiment. If one provokes by sharing a double vision of one's fingers and touches an object which is also clearly seen doubled we get not only the tactile impression of two objects but also the feeling that we have two fingers instead of one. This experiment shows that indeed a change in the optic picture of the body may change the postural model in its tactile aspect.

We should not believe that the postural model of the body is given in a static way. It is again and again the result of integration of different raw materials of tactile, kinesthetic and optic types. The material is chosen according to the whole situation. One should not say that this or that element is predominant. It is a living creation making use also of the infantile impressions and not a rigid unit. We create the shape of our whole body again and again according to the life situation. Klein and I have come to this result studying the so-called Japanese illusion (if hands and fingers of a subject are doubly twisted a pointed-to finger, especially of the left side, cannot be moved. Instead of it a finger of the other hand or of a nearby finger will be moved).[1]

There is not only the problem of what we know about the surface of our body but there is also the problem of what we know about the inner part of our body. I shall begin with the psychological aspects. If one asks an experienced subject what he knows about the inner part of the body one sees that we do not know anything about the inner part of the body. The only thing we feel is that there is some heavy substance. We feel nothing but the weight. In other words the inner part of the body is felt as a bag filled with a heavy substance. One can prove that very easily. If the subject is standing and we ask him about his head, he says he feels that there is something at the base of the head. The upper part of the head seems in some way not so well filled, and lighter than the deeper part of the head. If we order the person to lie down he feels at that very moment the substance floating towards the posterior occipital parts of the head which touch the ground. Quite the same thing occurs about the abdomen. When we are standing the heavy substance is in the iliacal parts. If we are lying down we feel the gravity towards the back whereas towards the stomach

[1] See Journal of Nervous and Mental Disease, **70**, 241, 1929.

the substance becomes lighter. We can see that we perceive our body quite in the same way as any other heavy substance. We perceive in the body the matter which is perceived as weight. We do not have any perception of what else is going on in the body. When we raise an arm at that moment we feel that weight is around the shoulder. When we put the arm down, it seems that something is running down and gravity is now about the hands, *i.e.*, these parts which are lower now. It is not only that alone but we can also say that our perception of the surface of our body is a very poor one. If we direct a person to close his eyes and to describe what is going on on the body we come to the paradox that we do not feel our skin, *i.e.*, the surface of our body. We feel the body only where there is some tension of the skin over a bone. Most of the subjects whose eyes are closed feel only the skin over the zygoma. Most of the parts of the body have a very blurred and indefinite surface and only where the body touches the external world do we get a clearer perception of our body. There is, however, again something which from a psychological point of view is of the utmost importance. If we touch the surface of any object we do not feel that there is immediate contact between the object and our fingers. If an experienced subject is asked to describe what is going on in himself he will say, he feels the object he touches; then there is nothing, *i.e.*, a free space, a free small space. After that we do not feel the skin but we feel something filled with this indefinite mass of weight. The problems are not only problems of experimental psychology, they are of enormous importance for the symptomatology of internal medicine. The parts where we are in special touch with the external world are felt better. We feel for instance the mouth. We feel the urinary desire. But we do not feel the urinary desire in the bladder, we feel it near to the external world, about one or two centimeters from the external urethral orifice. Quite the same thing is true about the bowels and the anal sensations. The desire to defecate is felt about two centimeters inside the anus. We can say that whenever we feel that something is going on in the body we do not feel it in the depths of the body but there is a projection to the surface. We can say that the living part of our body, the part of the body where we experience something, is very near to the surface, *i.e.*, one or two centimeters from the surface. That is a general law, as well for what is going on organically as for all psychogenic troubles. Hypochondriacal sensations are not experienced in the depths of the body but always near the surface. Or we can formulate it in a paradoxical way: We feel our body as a heavy substance, and this heavy substance has not a sharp outline toward the external world. Sometimes we feel something near to the external world, about one or two centimeters deep from the surface.

These statements are extremely important for the question of narcissism and of the different types of partial desires. Persons who, let us say, have strong anal desires have these places especially marked in their postural models. In the postural models of the body we shall find special representations for those partial desires which are increased. We have for instance to ask ourselves, What is the place of the urinary feelings in the postural model? What is the place of the anal desires in the postural model? What is the place of the sadistic desire and so on? I have the opinion that we can in some way read from the postural model of the body what partial desires in the individual are stronger than other ones. And we expect that whenever we find the trouble in one of the partial desires we shall find it marked in the postural model. In this respect it is, for instance, interesting to study the sensations that impotent patients have in their genitals. We can say that in the postural model of the body the genitals play a very important rôle. There is also the general idea that narcissism as well as the partial desires has its place in the postural model. We can study this too, in the way that we see what parts of the body remain in our consciousness or half-consciousness when we fall asleep. Federn has made the excellent observation that when we fall asleep we do not lose the knowledge of our whole body all at the same time. We lose knowledge of a part of our body and a part of the body remains in consciousness. Of course behind it there will be a special relation to some part of the body. This explains not a little part of neurotic symptomatology. Patients who have phantasies about returning to the maternal womb, before they fall asleep have a feeling that they become smaller and smaller. I have made one observation in which the patient finally thought she was not bigger than one centimeter.

Of course these problems are also in some way connected with the problem of the so-called " Head Zones " in internal medicine. Whenever there is an internal organ diseased there will be a change in the sensations of the skin. We do not live with the inner part of our body, we live in some way also not exactly with the surface of the body, but we live in a zone of the body one or two centimeters below the surface. This is at the same time a neurological, a psycho-analytic, and a general medical problem.

Only by considering the bodily scheme can we understand hysterical troubles of sensibility. There are, for instance, troubles of sensibility of the hand and of the sensibility of one side, especially the left side of the body. The postural model follows in its structure lay opinion concerning the body. The bodily scheme has an important access to the vasovegetative system. The vasovegetative system is influenced by the bodily scheme and when we find a symptomatic representation which follows the bodily scheme vasovegetative neurotic troubles will be found in the same region. I have observed a case of gastric ulcer in which heavy perspiration began exactly in the midline when the patient was in pain. Problems of the bodily scheme are at the same time problems of the distribution of vaso-vegetative troubles. Vasovegetative troubles have for the most part the topical relation that the bodily scheme has. One has to study problems of neurotic blushing—from a similar point of view. The tendency to exhibitionism is of course formed with relation to special parts of our bodily scheme. Here there is some special libidinous relation to the bodily scheme.

Analysis of the problem of the bodily scheme is incomplete if we do not appreciate the importance that motility has for the perception of our body. I may mention an experiment I have studied with Hoff. The individual puts both arms out horizontally. If I now raise one arm about forty-five deegrees above the horizontal line and the arm remains in this position for about thirty seconds and the subject is then requested to close the eyes and bring the raised arm to the same position as the horizontal one, then it will happen, with all normal persons, that the arm will not be brought back quite to the horizontal position but to a position nearer to the position of the raised arm. We call this experiment the persistence of posture. It is not a persistence of muscular tension, because if in the same experiment I put the one arm on a level below the horizontal and this arm remains there about thirty seconds also, and I then give the order to bring this lower arm to the same position as the horizontal arm, the subject will put the lower arm not so high as the horizontal one. It is not the persistence of the muscular tension but it is the persistence of the postural tendency. I would not have mentioned this experiment if it did not happen that at the same time not only the motility is changed but our knowledge about our own body is also changed. If I make this experiment and put the formerly raised arm passively on the same level as the horizontal arm, then the person will not feel that the arms are on the same level but that the arm which was raised before will appear now at a lower level than the other one. By the persistence of posture this position has become the normal position and every other posture is brought in relation with the attitude.

We can generally say that our postural model is changed by these muscular tensions. The postural model of the body is pulled in the direction of a special muscular tension, or the postural model of the body is dependent on muscular tensions. And the posture of our body has an enormous influence upon the knowledge of our body. That is again an important example for the general idea that we cannot clearly separate motility from the perception of our body. Every change in the tonus of our body changes at the same time also the knowledge we have of our body. It is very likely that the cerebellum as well as the postural apparatus in the medulla oblongata and the midbrain about which I have spoken so much influence also to a very high degree the postural model of our body.

But we can say that there is another very important law concerning the postural model of our body. Whenever we are in an unaccustomed position, the postural model of the body does not take account of it. We believe our body to be in the same position as is usual and we do not acknowledge the unaccustomed position of the body. The experiment that shows this very clearly is the so-called Aristotelian experiment. If we put a little ball between the two crossed fingers we feel two little balls and not one. In other words there are some movements that we do not take into the postural model of our body. Or we see the many things which are going on in our body. We do not take them into account. Many things in our body are ignored, or to make use of the psychoanalytic term, we repress many things which are going on in our motility. Many things going on in our body are repressed when they do not fit into the postural model of the body we have. We must get rid of that notion of repression which considers it as something extraordinary going on only on special occasions. We have the notion of our own body. We repress many things that do not belong in it. We repress, for instance, the fact that we have crossed the fingers. If I turn the head to the right side I still have a feeling that my face is directed towards the front. I repress the fact that the eyes are directed in the sidewise direction as long as the body is directed towards the front. We cannot understand such a simple thing as the knowledge of our own body if we do not say that we use some picture of our body and what is not necessary for the biological need or is biologically unaccustomed we do not make use of.

This problem of the postural model of the body goes deep into psychology but it also goes deep into the whole problem of sensibility. It is not true that we have sensations and that the sum of the sensations together makes us know what is going on within ourselves. Every sensation is brought in connection with the postural model of the body. We do not have an isolated sensation. As I have stated in the very beginning of the discussion, the postural model of the body is only possible by the great libido we have for our body, for every part of our body, but especially for the genital regions of our body. Every part of the body has its special representation and there is no doubt that the head plays a special part in the postural model of the body. We know that the single parts of the head play a special part in symbolization of another important part of the body, of the genitals. The problem of the psychoses which develop after operations on the eyes, on the genitals, on the female breast, is very closely connected with the question of the postural model of the body and the libido we give to special parts of the postural model of the body.

CHAPTER VII

POSTSCRIPT

Some General Remarks About the Relation of the Psychic and the Organic Apparatus

In the previous lectures we have spoken of the psychological aspect of the nervous apparatus as such. We shall now discuss the problem of organic disease in relation to the psychic life. We have to distinguish between these problems. When we have before us a case of multiple sclerosis at its beginning we find a mixture of organic and neurotic phenomena. Especially we shall find that such a disease very often begins with an hysterical astasia-abasia. What does such an occurence mean? We know that very often at the beginning of an organic disease we have not a real impairment of the function but when the function is going on there is some feeling of uncertainty about it, some greater strain in this function. We believe that the multiple sclerosis case does not have any organic troubles of equilibrium but when walking he feels that greater exertion than usual is necessary to keep the balance. When an organic case feels so, there are always complexes and those wild dissatisfied wishes of childhood, and when there is a tendency to conversion, the conversion will be directed into those parts of the body where he feels this organic strain. Or we would say that conversion goes to that point, where there is a feeling of strain, a feeling of uneasiness. This is what Freud calls the " somatisches Entgegenkommen," the somatic preparedness, or something in the organic sphere is prepared to meet the psychoneurotic tendencies. The astasia-abasia is based upon the queer feelings of uneasiness, the feeling that the function does not go on in the right way. That is the first step in the genesis of the conversion symptoms.

But now what happens in the case of multiple sclerosis if the conversion is directed toward the equilibrium? The hysterical astasia-abasia patient does not make use of some mechanism in the brain, a mechanism for coördination. These mechanisms are certainly organic; and I am of the opinion that the hysteric indeed does not make use in the right way of vestibular-cerebellar and frontal tonus and coördination mechanisms. Sometimes he does not make use of striopallidal mechanisms in the right way. I think all of you know those cases of hysteria that are tense in their muscles and have at the same time some tremor. We call these myotonoclonia trepidans. I personally think that in this myotonoclonia trepidans there must also be some impairment in the apparatus that has to do with the distribution of tonus. There is no difference in the apparatus, between organic and functional disease, but the organic disease acts continually whereas the psychic influence on this apparatus does not act continually but acts for a while, then passes, then acts again. It is more a difference in the quantity of the change than a difference in the apparatus on which the influence acts. We find conversion symptoms very often as long as the organic lesion is not yet developed and would not be sufficient to provoke a clear symptomatology. I think the cerebellar apparatus and the tonus apparatus are especially fit to draw to themselves the tendencies to conversion and therefore we find so often symptoms of hysterical hypertonus, symptoms of hysterical astasia and hysterical troubles of the equilibrium. The hysterical troubles of the equilibrium have very likely to do with the cerebellum and the medulla oblongata. This is the problem of multiple sclerosis, but we have some very similar problems in some cases of combined sclerosis. When I began to be interested in neurology I saw a patient with very marked trouble of the astasia-abasia type. He had only one sign of organic trouble, the Babinski reflex, and still the patient was treated in the clinic as a functional case and treated very thoroughly. Suddenly he developed a very serious palsy and died in a very short time. The autopsy showed a very well marked combined sclerosis that had involved the spinocerebellar tract.

When the organic disease as such is developed, it satisfies as such, if it is strong enough, the unconscious wishes and desires, whereas as long as the organic trouble is not well enough expressed then the individual is not satisfied because he will not get all the advantages of organic disease. By organic disease the individual gets more love and attention. He is again the center of the family. He can also rule the family in a better way. Besides that the feeling of guilt which in everyone is satisfied by organic disease, and finally all the complexes may find satisfaction in an organic symptom. Here is the interpretation of the fact that so many children after the organic disease has disappeared retain these symptoms as functional ones. For instance after the whooping cough is over the cough may still continue.

But we have not only to reckon with the fact that the beginning or slight trouble finds its magnified expression by psychic influence, but we have also to reckon with the fact that the psychic influence may repress the organic symptoms. I am quite convinced that we are not right when we say that our patients show more symptoms by their complexes than they would be obliged to show. They want to be healthy. We know that there is a tendency to compensation if the whole tendency of the individual is directed against the disease. For instance, some persons who have slight troubles in the equilibrium by a special degree of attention, a special biological need, can act as if the equilibrium troubles did not exist. All that we can say is that the psychic influence acts again on the same apparatus but this time not in the direction of the disease but against the direction of the disease. Then we get a picture in which the patient seemingly is normal and still he has an organic trouble, only this organic trouble is compensated by the psychic strength of the individual. This is, for instance, to be seen in postencephalitic cases who under the influence of some emotion suddenly lose their organic symptoms. Of course when the emotion has gone if the individual is unable to maintain the emotions in these directions, the organic trouble returns. The psychogenic influence acts on the same apparatus, but the psychogenic influence is not strong enough to counteract the continual influence of the change in the apparatus which is going on from the organic disease as such. We have always to consider that all the problems about which we speak are not only problems of the quality of the influence but also problems of the quantity of the influence. It is often true that such a compensatory tendency concerning the organic disease, such as compensatory " health " cannot be maintained for a long time. Sometimes of course the psychic compensation does not act on the same apparatus which is diseased but works in another way. We have also to say that there exists not only a psychogenic disease but also a psychogenic health, so to speak. That plays an important part in some cerebellar cases and it also plays an important part in some encephalitis cases. But I would like to say that very likely in cerebellar cases, the psychogenic health may, if the tendency to compensation persists, and the organic trouble does not increase, become by and by also an organic health. The compensatory tendencies of the other parts of the brain become stronger and stronger and very likely there exists also not only a possibility of psychic compensation but the psychic compensation can be in these cases at the same time a compensation which goes on in the organism. In some of the cases of congenital cerebellar disease it has been described that after the destruction of the cerebellum the pyramidal tract is increased in size and in volume (Anton). Here is a problem of psychogenic compensation but this problem is very closely connected with the problem of organic compensation as we see it clearly in cases of lack of cerebellum with increased pyramidal tracts. If we remove one kidney the other shows a marked degree of compensation. What we see as psychogenic health, as I mentioned, is only one instance of the compensatory functions of the individual. Compensatory functions are not only in the psyche and the brain but in the whole organism. What we can study in the brain in a very clear way is also to be found in the functions of the other parts of the organism.

But all these problems we have spoken of are not problems concerning compensation of function only. We have in addition to the problem of compensation of function also the problem, how can the disease as such be influenced by psychogenic factors? This problem is quite different. I personally am not convinced that the disease multiple sclerosis can be influenced by psychogenic factors, and I am very much in doubt whether it is possible to influence the post-encephalitic disease by psychic measures. Let us make it clear what this means—a disease like multiple sclerosis or a disease like encephalitis. We might say that from a general biological point of view it is a fight of the organism against something which belongs to the outer world. This something might be bacteria, or changes in the blood vessels through toxic influences. These changes are going on in a place in the organism which is very likely very far from the processes in the organism which we can understand and it is very difficult to say whether this deep lying process in the organism, this part of the physiological process that is going on can be influenced by a psychogenic mechanism. It is not a question which we can settle without experience. It is a matter of experience. I personally think that the combat of the brain against the spirochete or the invisible virus can be understood as something going on in the organism, which after all is a psycho-physiological organism. But these layers are very different from the layers in which we can grasp in a clear way the psychogenic influences. I am very much in doubt whether it is possible to influence this deep layer of the organic conflict of the individual by the layer in which the psychic conscious and instinctive unconscious processes are going on.

When we come to the general problem, what is the psychic influence, and what has the psychic influence to do with an organic change, I may quote some excellent ideas of Bleuler. Bleuler has written an article about abreaction and occasional apparatus (Gelegenheitsapparat). He means by this term a psycho-physical apparatus which is built up for a special occasion. He says if we find an individual who has hysterical fits and if she always gets them when she sees special persons, *e.g.,* when she sees a policeman, what does such a psychic apparatus mean? Bleuler says that she has the fit very often and still she does not finish her reaction. The abreaction does not come. What is the reason for this? Why does she not abreact the psychic energy spent in the hysterical fit? It is only necessary to see one hysterical fit to know that a great deal of energy is spent. It is not the spending or the non-spending of the energy. There is something else in the case I have mentioned. The girl had a relation with a policeman who hypnotized her and had sex intercourse with her. Finally there were difficulties in this hypnotic and sexual relation. Psychoanalytically we would say, her difficulties are based on the disappointment which took place in early life with her father. But by these events there is built up a wrong switch for the psychic energy, or a wrong shifting over of all the sex energy. Or the events of life—present life and the life in childhood—bring about a shifting of the energy to the wrong paths. Whenever energy in the psyche and the body is produced and is near to be used or exploded, this energy will always go more into the wrong paths because of this occasional apparatus, which makes a wrong shifting over. We have to destroy the *Gelegenheitsapparatus,* occasional apparatus, and we do that by psychoanalysis, finding out what has produced this apparatus. Such an occasional apparatus is indeed on the borderline between functional and organic.

We can say that the organic lesion causes something quite similar. Most organic lesions build up a wrong shifting over of the psychic energy. The psychic energy always goes into the wrong path. Bleuler is right in saying it is a *Gelegenheits*-apparatus, an occasional apparatus, because very likely these processes of building an occasional apparatus are indeed processes which are very near to the organic processes of building up an organ. Very likely an organ is in some way also an occasional apparatus, the organ being built up in the same way as such an occasional apparatus. The occasional apparatus indeed will be in connection with some vasovegetative phenomena and will be in connection with the knowledge of some parts of the body. We can also say the organic structures are built by apparatuses which very likely once were occasional apparatuses. That is our general conception. Whether it is possible to influence an organic apparatus by a newly built occasional apparatus, that is a matter of experience in an individual case.

The forces of the occasional apparatus and the forces of the organic apparatus are in some way of the same order but not all on the same level. Of course every part of the body is under the influence of the blood vessels and the vegetative system. But there are some parts of the body which are rather rigid and farther distant from the psychic level. Then there are others which are in immediate connection with psychic life with the conscious as well as the unconscious. Every organ and every apparatus can be influenced in some way because we know that the organic as well as the psychic (psychogenic) apparatus is in connection with the diencephalon, which again is in rather deep connection with all these organic parts of the body. Many years ago I tried to interpret the so-called psychological phenomena of hypnosis on such an hypothesis. I tried to show what we know psychoanalytically, that hypnosis is related to the infantile attitude of the individual. The hypnotizer becomes in some way an image for the father, especially the omnipotent father. The psychic attitude is at the same time an attitude which is in connection with some primitive part of the brain, *i.e.,* with those parts of the brain which are in connection with the sleeping center and in connection with the primitive apparatus of tonus. This is an instance of what we could call a psycho-physiological integration. And we can say that the problem of hypnosis is a problem of a special type of transference and at the same time a problem of a special apparatus in the brain. And of course it is of very great interest to know that the phenomena of hypnosis persist in animals whose cortex has been removed. One can even produce a hypnosis in animals when only the brainstem with the nucleus ruber is preserved and the other parts of the brain are removed. Again we see that hypnosis is a problem of the brain. It is at the same time also a problem of transference and some psychic attitudes. Regression has an organic background we can grasp. We have the general opinion that the psychic apparatus and the apparatus of the brain and the apparatus of the whole organism are of the same order but not of the same level.

LITERATURE

Only a small part of the literature can be mentioned here. Many references are to be found in my " Medizinische Psychologie," Springer, Berlin, 1924 (especially lectures 4, 5, and 6)—a great part of the literature to lectures 1, 2, 3, is reported in the book by Hoff and Schilder, " Die Lagereflexe des Menschen," Springer, Wien, 1927. One who is especially interested in the postural model of the body may read my little book on the " Körperschema," Springer, Berlin, 1923. A survey of the problems of Sleep can be found in my paper " Über Psychosen bei chronischer Encephalitis Epidemica nebst Bemerkungen über Bezichungen psychischer Vorgänge zu organischen Strukturen," Zeits. f. d. ges. Neur. u. Psych., 118, 29. In the same volume the description of the case of Cortical Encephalitis can be found which is briefly reported in the third lecture. A good orientation on the problems of Sleep and Consciousness may be gotten from the articles on sleep in the Jahreskurse für ärztliche Fortbildung, 1929, Lehman, München (papers by Poetzl and v. Economo). Also v. Economo, Schlaftheorie Ergebnisse der Physiologie, 28, 1929; Pawlow, Skandinav. Arch. f. Physiologie, 1923; Reichardt, Hirnstam und Psyche, Monat. f. Psych. u. Neur., 68, 1928; Kleist, Über episodische Dämmerzustände, Thiele, Leipzig; Miller, Mental dissociation, its relation to catatonia and the mechanism of narcolepsy, Brain, 50, 27; Richter, C. P., Pathol. sleep and similar conditions studied by the method of electric skin resistance, Arch. of Neur. and Psych., Vol. 21, 1929.

Concerning hypnosis see my book with Kauders, the translation of which has appeared in this Monograph Series.

As for the problems of tone see, too, my paper with Hoff, Zur Kenntnis der Symptomatologie vestibulärer Erkrankungen, Deut. Zeit. f. Nervenheilk., 103, 1928. A complete report of the paper of Goldstein and his co-workers may be found in the book by Hoff and Schilder.

About Antrieb (impulses) besides the papers by Gerstmann and Schilder, see, too, Jelliffe, The Mental Picture in Schizophrenia and in Epidemic Encephalitis, American Jour. of Psychiatry, 6, 1927; Parker, Choreatische Erscheinungen und Steigerung der Haltungs und Stellreflexe bei akuter Cocain intoxication, Deut. Zeit. f. Nervenh., 103; Benedek, Zwangmässiges Schreien als postencephalitische Hyperkinesien, Zeitsc. f. d. g. Neur. u. Psych., 1925; E. Straus, Untersuchungen über die postchoreatischen Motilitätsstörungen, Monats. f. Psych. u. Neur., 66, 1927.

On Depersonalization see Schilder, Selbstbewusstsein und Persönlichkeitsbewusstsein, Springer, Berlin, 1914; Psychische Symptomen bei Mittel und Zwischenhirn Erkrankungen, Wien. klin. Woch., 1927, No. 36; E. Stern, Über psychische Zwangsvorgänge und ihre Entstehung bei encephalitischen Blickkrämpfen, Arch. f. Psych., 81, 1927; Stengel, Zur Klinik und Pathophysiologie des postencephalitischen Blickkrampfes, Monats. f. Psych. u. Neur., 70, 1928; Jelliffe, Psychological Components in Postencephalitic Oculogyric Crises, Arch. of Neur. and Psych., 21, 491, 1929; On Amnesias see W. White: Retraction Theory from a Psychological Standpoint, Transactions of the American Medico-Psychological Association, 6, 1899; R. Stern, Ueber die Aufhellungen von retrograden Amnesien, Zeits. f. d. g. Neurol. u. Psych., 108, 1927; Schilder, Zur Lehren von den Amnesien, Arch. f. Psych., 72, 1924.

On Pharmacology: H. Hartmann, Cocainismus und Homosexualität, Zeits. f. d. g. Neur. u. Psych., 95, 1925; and my paper on Psychotherapie bei Psychosen, I Kongress für Psychotherapie, Marhold, Halle.

On Optic Agnosia, see the book by Poetzl, Optische Agnosie, Handbuch für Psychiatrie von Aschaffenburg, 1928, and his paper "Experimentell erzeugte Traumbilder, Zeits. f. d. g. Neur. und Psych., 37, 1912; Schilder, Medizinische Psychologie.

A good review is H. Klüver, Visual Disturbances After Cerebral Lesions, Psychological Bulletin, 24, 1927.

On the Postural Model: Hartmann and Schilder, Körperinneres und Körperschema, Zeits. f. d. g. Neur. u. Psych., 109, 666, 1927; Gerstmann, Finger agnosie u. isolierte Agraphie, Zeits. f. d. g. Neur. u. Psych., 108, 1927; Klein und Schilder, Japanese Illusion and Postural Model of the Body, Journal of Nervous and Mental Disease, 1929; W. Riese, Ueber die sogenannte Phantomhand der Amputierten, Deut. Zeit. f. Nerven., 101, 270, 1927.

PART TWO
THE RELATION BETWEEN THE PERSONALITY
AND MOTILITY OF SCHIZOPHRENICS

PART TWO

THE RELATION BETWEEN THE PERSONALITY AND MOTILITY OF SCHIZOPHRENICS *

CHAPTER VIII

ACTUAL CAUSES AND REGRESSION IN NEUROSIS AND PSYCHOSIS

In every psychoneurosis there are actual conflicts. When the actual problem cannot be solved, the old problems of childhood will appear again; we then speak of regressions. The regression goes back to important events of child life. These events may be of importance in themselves or the individual constitution may give importance to events of childhood which in themselves are not so extraordinary. We call those important events of childhood " points of fixation " and mean with this term also the level of sexual development in which those events took place. In hysteria the actual conflict may be a love affair; the point of fixation is given by an Œdipus complex too strongly developed. By regression the Œdipus complex is revived but the individual does not allow himself to live it through and the Œdipus complex is only symbolically realized in the hysterical symptom (for instance, an hysterical fit). A. Meyer has often emphasized that the difference between a psychoneurosis and a schizophrenia is not a fundamental one. Among the psychasthenics of Pierre Janet, as Jung has pointed out, there were many schizophrenics (or shall we say, schizophrenic developments?).

We have therefore the right to study schizophrenia on the same principles as in psychoneurotic cases. From a psychoanalytic point of view we therefore ask in every case: What are the actual problems? What are the points of fixation? In what way does the regression take place? Are there actual problems and conflicts in every case of schizophrenia which determine the beginning of a schizophrenic attack? What is a psychic trauma? In the beginnings of psychoanalysis, importance was given only to the spectacular events of life, an assault, a breach of promise, sudden danger of life or the

* Lectures held before the staff of the Phipps Psychiatric Clinic.

death of beloved relatives. But life does not consist of great events only. The numberless daily problems are of greater importance. There is the problem of sex always with us; there are so many wishes we have to be resigned about; a fight or struggle against the hostilities of our companions and co-workers; a fight between love and hatred in ourselves. In brief there is always the problem of adaptation to the always varying reality with its manifold situations. Adaptation is chiefly an adaptation to our fellow beings. Adaptation to what is not alive goes with adaptation to our fellow beings, who live in reality.

We have to consider from this point of view different levels of development. Puberty as such calls for many adaptations. The individual has to cope with an enormously increased sex desire and at the same time also with other new interests that come up. There are new forces, new aims. But the individual does not know how to balance energy and work. Another important step has to lead from the vague and indistinct sex activity of puberty to real sex life. At this time the important decision concerning one's calling has to be made. I point only to various difficulties in the choice of the objects in adult persons and in the foundation of the family. Involution also, especially in women, again raises enormous problems. Resignation, a new life, new aims, are again called for. Thus every age of man has its specific set of problems and difficulties which call for specific adaptations. All our problems stand in close relation with the problem of the family. Psychoanalysis has shown clearly that all the experiences of early childhood are in some way mediated by the medium of the family and the early life problems are problems concerning the family. Only through the family does the child get into relations with society. The period of latency, after the sixth year, and the period of puberty and the choice of the love object imply the task of getting rid of the family influence and loosening the family ties. Then comes the foundation of a family of one's own and all the difficulties of the education of children and their breaking away from the family. Every family problem always has an economic side. Sexual and economic independence very often go parallel with each other. The death of the father makes a new psychic adaptation necessary. I have the impression that the death of the father is very often of greater influence on the individual's fate than the death of the mother. This is very likely due to the specific social structure of our culture in which the father is the real connecting link with society. This is a superficial scheme. Every phase in all these adaptations contains also pure sex problems in themselves. Puberty, adolescence, involution carry their special sex problems. There are many possibilities for dissatisfaction, and also moral conflicts in the course of every life. From such a point of view we have also to consider the difficulties of schizophrenics.

In one of the cases I shall discuss (that of L.R., a girl of eighteen years), the difficulty began in puberty. The sex problem overcame her when she became aware of two pregnancies in her family. One of her sisters and a sister-in-law became pregnant about the same time. The family lived very close together so that she was very much impressed by these events. About the same time she had her first menstruation. The first menstruation is in most girls' lives a problem of very great importance. Most of them are not well prepared and they get frightened. A feeling of guilt appears. They think that some disease has come to punish them for feelings they have in connection with sex. The feelings of guilt in connection with every sex activity are of enormous strength. Disease appears in our unconscious as a punishment for our guilt. Pious persons believe that diseases are sent by God in order to punish individuals for their sins. Every disease therefore also gives the satisfaction of punishment, which makes the feeling of guilt easier. Menstruation provokes fear in the patient, she believes there may be something wrong with her and she enters into another position in relation to the world.

Whenever we are in some way deeply concerned with anything, we change our attitude towards the world. It is probable that if we wish to have a real perception, if we wish to be really interested in our own thoughts, then we must in some way do so in accordance with ourselves; and whenever an emotion sets in which is too strong for us, it takes away something of the interest we might have for the world, which then appears to be changed. This is the problem of what we call *depersonalization*. Not only the world appears to be changed but at the same time one's own personality undergoes an important change. One seems to be more lifeless, more an automaton, more mechanical. This feeling of being mechanical is almost always in connection with a deep undercurrent of emotion. This hinders us in actualizing and sensing all our other tendencies and all our other strivings. Our patient has not only had feelings of guilt concerning menstruation, but the pregnancy of her sister made her feel that she might be pregnant herself. She began to realize some queer sensations in her abdomen; it felt tense.

What may such a delusion mean? Of course every person is afraid of the sex difficulty he may meet, and every girl admires another one who got pregnant and has so shown her ability in sex. Behind this lies the great admiration for the mother; the wish of taking a place like that of the mother. This is a tendency to identification with the mother, which is a part of the Œdipus complex of the girl.

In this case the wife of the older brother, and the older sister— two persons extremely apt to be taken as substitutes for her mother— provoke in her the wish to be as these persons are. In addition to this: her older brother was in fact the substitute in the family for the father, who had died early. In the fancied pregnancy of our patient there lies not only an identification with the sister and sister-in-law but also one with the mother. The patient never told who might be the father of her expected child. But one of the first signs of her psychosis was that she refused to eat with her older brother, who after the father's early death, as stated, was the chief of the family. She believes that he knew all her thoughts. She may have considered him in her unconscious as the expected child's father.

Is such a development in puberty something very unusual? Is this something we would have to count in with the symptomatology of schizophrenia? Or is this something we might find also in the neuroses? At the time of puberty similar fancies are not unusual, and I should warn against making a diagnosis of schizophrenia on the ground of illusions of this kind.

The most striking instance of this type I have met in a neurotic person, was in the case of a homosexual. He was a rather intelligent boy of about twenty-two, of a very active sexuality. At the age of eighteen, after homosexual intercourse, he got a hemorrhoidal inflammation and had difficulties in defecating. He fancied that he had become pregnant and would get the Nobel Prize for this pregnancy. This was a delusion he retained for a while but dropped later.

We find similar delusions not too rarely. The significance of such a delusion varies according to the relation it has to the rest of the personality and to the place it has in the whole psychic life. If it is in the center of the whole personality it has quite a different meaning from when the central personality has other tendencies and the delusion takes more or less the part of a play in which the individual indulges for a while. In the case of L.R. the patient not only had the illusion but she also lived fully in the illusion. We should always ask whenever we meet a psychic content, does the individual live fully in the psychic content or is there some part of the individual not living fully in the psychic content?

It is important to consider from this point of view illusions and hallucinations which we provoke in hypnosis. As far as my own experience goes the individual always remains critical with a part of his whole personality, and the hallucinations in hypnosis never obtain the same importance for the individual as the hallucinations of the schizophrenic. There may be a hypnotized patient and you suggest to him anxiety and fear, making him hallucinate a snake or a lion, and still, in some way, the patient will have the consciousness in himself that the snake and lion have no full reality. There are differences between the illusion of a hysteric, the illusion of a psychopathic individual, the illusion of puberty and the illusion of the schizophrenic.

In psychoanalytic terminology we can formulate it as follows: the Ideal Ego and the Ego agree more or less completely with the delusion (hallucination, illusion). The delusion is based on the breaking through of unconscious wishes into consciousness.

But I wish to return to the history of our patient. Very soon she dropped this illusion of being pregnant and at the same time she became interested in girls. She had a crush especially for a classmate of hers, and got the feeling that all the people knew about her wishes. We see very often that the homosexual makes an effort to attain heterosexuality before the homosexual component comes out clearly. It is in this case as if this delusion of pregnancy were the last effort of being like her mother. She must have felt that she could not be like her mother. In my experience it is very often a feeling of inferiority and insufficiency which hinders many homosexuals from taking the place of the parent of the same sex. There may be very different reasons why such a feeling of insufficiency arises. In one of my cases the father was very brutal and used to maltreat the mother as well as the boy. He used also to laugh at the child and to ridicule him. He was of enormous strength, and the boy had the opportunity of observing the father during intercourse and got in some way the feeling that he could not equal the father. He felt compelled therefore to take the place of the mother. In compensation he tried to become strong intellectually and he tried in such a way to become superior to his male friends, who were substitutes for the father. His homosexual cathexis resulted partly from the feeling of hatred against the father and partly was in connection with the idea that he would never be able to display the same strength as his father.

A female patient of mine had a father who was a very good character, but he used to like to play with the children by wrestling, and on such occasions she experienced an enormous feeling of inferiority. When she was about three or four years old she had an opportunity to observe the father's penis, which made a very great impression on her and she felt that she wanted to be like the father. She wanted to take his place, which attitude was reinforced by the fact that she wrestled in a similar way with her own younger brother. She got the feeling that she had to be superior like her father was and had to take the masculine part. Finally she developed an idea that she had to behave in a similar way towards women. But she felt also she would never be attractive enough to attract men and she could never be as desirable as other girls.

All these cases escape from heterosexuality as our patient does because of their feeling that they will not be able to fufill the part of their own sex. It seems too difficult for them. But strong heterosexual tendencies have primarily been present. In our patient, too, we assume these heterosexual tendencies in her earlier childhood. As I shall show later the heterosexual delusion of pregnancy need not, however, be the expression of a primary heterosexuality.

But what made the patient shun heterosexuality? Her father was rather rough; he often spanked her. In one of the few dreams reported that fact came out. Her father forbade her also very severely to play with boys. These two facts drove her away from heterosexuality. But there is another very important fact. Up to puberty she slept with her mother and enjoyed the feeling of her mother's body. We then can understand that the patient built up a tendency to homosexuality; too great a fear concerning the father, too great an attraction to the mother and very likely an exaggerated idea about the difficulties of taking the place of the mother.

But the psychosis begins with a seemingly increased heterosexuality. How can we interpret this? The primary heterosexuality of the infantile Œdipus complex has been jeopardized by the facts about which I have spoken. With puberty the homosexuality is near to break through again.

One can say that the idea of pregnancy which preceded the homosexual tendency is an attempted overcompensation of homosexual tendencies which were already under way before they appeared in the consciousness of the patient. In the beginning of schizophrenia we often see shooting up seemingly strong heterosexuality. But if we examine more carefully, the heterosexuality is not at all strong.

The patients endeavor to escape homosexuality by exaggerating heterosexuality. I have seen a patient running around in the streets seeking his fiancée—after all an unusual way to find one's fiancée—and after having done this for a while he heard voices telling him that he was a homosexual.

Others show an exaggerated love for persons whom they cannot reach in any way. They want to assure themselves that they are heterosexuals; out of their weakness it is necessary for them to exaggerate. One of my schizophrenic patients when he was fighting a very long time against his partly unconscious homosexuality, began relations with his landlady who was about fifteen or twenty years older than he and was at the same time an image of his mother. The schizophrenia broke out with jealousy against the landlady whom he accused of having sex relations with her niece.

The first symptoms the patient L.R. had were the expression of a tendency to overcompensate her homosexuality. As I have indicated, one of the first signs of the psychosis was that she did not want to eat with her brother, because she believed her brother knew of her homosexual thoughts and her pregnancy. But why does she feel that her thoughts also are known to all the other persons? This is one of the common symptoms in the beginning of schizophrenia and we bring it in connection with what we call in psychoanalysis the loss of the borderline of the personality. Here we come to one of the central problems of this case; this is the problem of what schizophrenia might be from the point of view of regression. Of course we have also to ask ourselves what does the homosexuality of this patient mean?

We know some facts of fixation which played a rôle in the homosexuality of the patient. But the loss of the "borderline" is more difficult to interpret. The patient feels that her feelings are well known to the brother; she thinks, too, that there is an electric current going on by which she is in connection with the ward physician and the ward physician thus influences her. She influences the other patients in a similar way. It is remarkable that at the very beginning of the homosexual attack an elderly woman provoked in her feelings she compared with those provoked by an electric current. There is also a double stream going from her to the others and from the others to her. She knows the thoughts of the others and by her thoughts she prevents the others from getting comforted. It is interesting that the patient has the feeling that she can sometimes control her thoughts so that the others are not influenced. But it is impossible to learn from her what this control consists of. There must be some indescribable psychic events. Another patient of mine said she made other patients cough. But it was impossible for her to say how she did it. The patient in these thoughts goes back to the state of narcissism. The narcissistic stage is a stage in which the individual does not draw a sharp line between subject and object, and we suppose that the infant immediately after birth does not have a clear notion of what is going on in the world. It knows perhaps a little better what is going on in the body.

The psychoanalytic formulation is that the child at that time knows only its own body, a formulation which I think is not correct. I should rather say that subject and object must exist for the child but the borderline between subject and object is not a sharp borderline. Of course if there is not a clear world there will not be much interest in such a world, and if there is a better knowledge of one's own body one's own body will be more the center of interest. This knowledge of one's own body will be permeated by the whole sex activity. At this time the sex activity is not yet concentrated on the genitals and is therefore diffusely spread about the whole body. This is of course a piece of constructive psychology. We have no comments of infants about such things. It may nevertheless be worth while to stress the difference between this part of our psychology and what we know about homosexuality in this case. Of course if we had a complete regression to such a narcissistic stage we would have before us an individual who is like an imperfect being, or who is like an infant, which is not the case with our patient. There is only the loss of the borderlines which we can call narcissistic. We can also speak of an identification with the houghts of the other. It is as if what the one person knows is also known by the other person. We come to the rather important formulation, that the tendency to identification with other persons is rather diffuse and vague in these narcissistic stages. We know that the tendency to imitation in children is indeed very great. They not only identify themselves with their parents, smile when others smile, laugh when others laugh, cry when others cry, but they even make the same movements that living and even non-living objects make, whatever may appear in the surroundings of such a being. But there arises immediately the great question, what are the fixating factors, why under the actual difficulty of puberty, does the regression go back not only to homosexuality but also to the more primitive narcissistic stage? What are the fixating elements? What are the reasons for such a deep narcissistic regression? We cannot give an answer based on experience to this question because we do not know anything about the specific events in the infant's life, and we know even less about the specific events in the embryonic life. Therefore we can only speak in a rather vague way in such cases about the fixation whereas the other fixation, that in homosexuality, is something which is rather concrete; our ideas about the point of fixation at the narcissistic level are not based upon experience in the same way as our ideas about points of fixation in other stages of development.

All these electric currents, all these influences by thoughts our patient complains about stand in rather close relation to her sex wishes. She sometimes has said and then has withdrawn it, that these thoughts of the others go into her vagina and come out of her vagina. I have mentioned already that she has compared her homosexual feelings to an electric current. In such patients we find in connection with this primitive loss of the borderline of the ego a diffuse sexualization of the human relations. One of the patients of my own observation had the feeling that all the sex life going on in the world is finally her own sex life, and she enjoys every intercourse taking place in the world. The child borne by her sister is a child she has borne because she has felt the pleasure in herself when her brother-in-law had intercourse with her sister. Our patient L.R. has heard many people speaking about her. She heard her physician (a woman) say, "Ridiculous child." Patient says: Dr. Squ. is asking me to write down everything I hear. Dr. Squ. sends her to the insane asylum, poor child," or " when did you begin that ridiculous child," or " write down everything I say," or " You are not serious in them L——, when I tell you to write down these things. You believe everything I say. However, I wait, I am going to send you to the lunatic asylum. That is enough for this morning. You have answered with your own thoughts L—— poor child, Miss N. is going to take you to the lunatic asylum to-morrow."

These are not real hallucinations—they are something in between a representation and a hallucination, as most of the hallucinations we meet in our patients are not really perceptions; most of the hallucinations are near to the so-called eidetic pictures of *Jaensch*. That the patient is addressed as " poor child " and gets orders makes it probable that these voices are in close relation with the dissolution of the Ideal Ego (Super Ego). Her Ideal Ego criticises her for being a half-wit; her Ideal Ego tells her to write things down; her Ideal Ego says, " You shall believe all that I tell you." We come to the general and important conclusion that whenever we find a considerable degree of regression at the same time we shall also find that there is something going on in the Ideal Ego. The Ideal Ego can not be destroyed completely. Therefore, the patient worries so much that she might be "a half-wit." Therefore, the voices are always saying she is a half-wit, she will be sent into the asylum and so on.

This type of voices appeared at first in connection with an older neighbor of hers. She was in love with Dr. Squ., her ward physician. She has also an important position among the persons who send her those voices. An Ideal Ego exists in her, but the Ideal Ego has undergone some change. This Ideal Ego of the patient tries to take her away from her homosexuality and from her diffuse sexuality. The interpretation of one of her dreams makes it very obvious that she tries to escape the homosexual relations with the other patients. *She throws down a vase and with the help of Dr. Squ. goes into another room descending a ladder.*

There is a strong transference to Dr. Squ. in this dream. I want to emphasize that there is no complete regression to the narcissistic level. Combined with this very deep regression to a very early stage, there are other regressions not so deep. We shall never understand these cases if we speak of only *one* point of fixation. Of course it is always of great importance to determine what is the deepest point of fixation. But this deepest point of fixation does not determine the whole symptomatology. It is based upon other fixations also. In this case the homosexual fixation has come out in a rather clear way. We cannot count, in any psychic treatment, on coming to the fixating events of the narcissistic phases—but we can count on being able to do something about other points of fixation, and very likely this is one of the possibilities of psychotherapy in this case.

Another important question in such a case is, how can we get a transference with such a patient? Of course, there is not a complete regression to the narcissistic stage. Her interest is not limited to her own personality; there will always be some interest for other persons; there will always be some part of the Ideal Ego available, some transference possible, and with these remainders of the transference we have to work. In what way is the transference of such a person different from the transference of the neurotic case?

I wish to repeat in a few short sentences the way which we have taken. We began with the actual difficulty, which in this case consisted in the adaptation to puberty. This actual difficulty cannot be solved by the patient because of points of fixation which lie in the homosexuality, and therefore regression takes place to the homo-sexuality. The patient, in the beginning, tries to overcompensate by an increased heterosexuality but fails with that, and the regression does not only go to the homosexuality but goes to the narcissistic level. This regression to the narcissistic level leads to the loss of borderline between the personality and other persons, and at the same time we find changes in the Ideal Ego which come out in the way the voices talk to her. Some parts of the Ideal Ego are preserved. There exists also some possibility of transference.

CHAPTER IX

ON TRANSFERENCE IN SCHIZOPHRENIA

As in this case, we often find hallucinations in connection with the Ideal Ego. When the Ideal Ego is built up in the personality, there remains always some difference between the Ideal Ego and the other parts of the personality. We speak about the voice of conscience, and the voice of conscience always remains separated from the rest of the personality. This is indeed a beginning hallucination. To this group belongs also the " Daimonion of Socrates " and we know that the identifications which build up the Ideal Ego of the individual do not blend completely with the personality and therefore when projections take place, those persons who, at first, have been introjected by identification are then pushed out again. Whatever has come to us by identification gets projected easily by the individual.

Hallucinations which are related to the Ideal Ego do not have the same clinical significance as other hallucinations. I have, for instance, observed a hysterical patient who had fever during the night and she saw a fat person sitting on her bed—the patient was herself rather fat—who ordered her not to be lazy and to get up. The next morning the patient awoke with a hysterical astasia and abasia. The Ideal Ego in this case, in the figure of the fat woman, fought against her laziness, against her hysterical tendency to astasia and abasia, but was too weak. Persons who are almost normal or belong to the hysterical group suddenly hear a voice say, " Don't do that." Moral voices which stand in close relation to the Ideal Ego have not a very bad prognostic significance.

Now we come to the general question of the transference in cases which reach the narcissistic level in their regression. When one begins to treat such patients, they follow one to a certain degree, but very soon one feels there is something between the patient and the physician that keeps the patient from following completely, or the transference is very often not a complete one, sometimes in patients who from an ordinary point of view are rather well adapted.

I have, for instance in my mind, a patient who complained chiefly that she had lost her feelings and her interests and that she had become stupid. This patient behaved at first in a rather nice way. She answered questions and went to the theater, but when she went into theaters she very often got a terrible feeling that she did not understand at all what was going on and she developed serious states of anxiety. She sometimes felt persecuted in the street, with a terrible feeling of anxiety. For the first hours I spoke with the patient, she answered rather well, but very soon there was no progress in the discussion. It was as if a wall had been erected between me and the patient. That is, the phenomenon one rather often meets in patients who have a schizophrenia. Very often we cannot get over it with our technique. We then have either to change the technique and begin in a non-psychoanalytic way or we have to wait, or even to give up.

This lack of transference shows an enormous difference from the attitude of the neurotic. I would not say that it is always so in our schizophrenic patients, but it is so in rather a great number of them, and this hinders the psychoanalysis of such patients. I shall compare, for instance, the transference in the case of B., a psychopathic patient, with noisy fits of anger and violence with the transference of a progressive schizophrenic. In the case of B., the transference increased. It is sometimes a positive or a negative one; it can be handled. The lack of transference in the schizophrenic patients is in connection with the fact that they are too much concerned with themselves or that they are too narcissistic. Therefore, they do not offer a satisfactory amount of libido for the object. The more the love of their own person (narcissistic libido) increases, the more the love to the other persons (object libido) diminishes. That is somewhat schematic because we must reckon with the fact that, as I have mentioned, the regression in the schizophrenic to the narcissistic stage is never a complete one. There are always maintained some relations to the outward world, and if these relations are closer, then in some cases we may build up a transference of sufficient degree. " Narcissistic transference " does not exist. Narcissistic means no object transference. But, maybe, there might come a transference which is not in connection with the deepest point of regression, but in connection with the other deeper or higher points of fixation. We could, for instance, suppose that a patient of the type of L.R. may develop a homosexual transference which might sometimes be of a rather high intensity. It may have been that a female psychoanalyst would have got a deeper transference. Indeed, the transference to Dr. Squ., the ward physician, was rather strong.

Whether this remainder of object libido would have been strong enough to carry on a psychoanalysis is difficult to judge.

We have always to reckon with these difficulties in the transference which come from the fact that some part of the libido is narcissistic and is not available at all for the purpose of transference. But in almost every case we find some transference; sometimes it will be heterosexual, sometimes of a more primitive level. The homosexual schizophrenic whom I have mentioned had an excellent transference toward me. This transference in the first phases of the treatment—it was in 1927—indeed, led to a considerable improvement as he lost his delusional homosexual jealousy; he had great confidence in me. Then came a very characteristic dream in which *I tried to hypnotize him, and he defended himself, taking the chair to beat me.* The transference here entered the magic sphere. The patient protests in this dream against his passivity, against his being in some way the object of a magical homosexual action on my part, as indeed the hypnosis might be. The patient now became very uneasy when he came to me. He felt influenced by me in a mysterious way. All his great anxiety was in some way brought into connection with me. At this time there occurred a very interesting dream: *I show him a tube in which tablets had been and I tell him that tube has the name of Miroklet and I have poisoned some persons with this tube of Miroklet.* I asked especially for associations to Miroklet and the associations were the following: Herakles—Heraklet—athlet. The next association was that Miroklet has very likely to do with mirum (Latin), something wonderful. It was very likely that miroklet meant something in connection with my sex organ. I once presented him with a tube of adalin. There is something poisonous about it. Ambivalent transference set in. The patient refused to eat and very often had the fear that he might be poisoned not only by me but by almost any person who plays an important part in his life—mother, landlady, father. The patient would never eat anything some one else had cooked but only what he had cooked himself and he ate mostly things which, like sausage, are ready-made. This is a very primitive type of transference, the transference which is homosexual, where the homosexuality is connected with magic fears. This is one instance of a schizophrenic type of transference. Stärke reports a patient whose transference consisted in beating the physician in his face. We have, of course, the idea that in such sadistic attacks there is an effort on the part of the patients to come nearer to the actual world. In comparison with stupor, they indicate progress, but such types of transference of course are not always very agreeable for the physician. There is only one transference you can really work with; that is transference on the Oedipus level.

I wish now to give a short report about the transference of another interesting case of schizophrenia I observed about two years ago. The patient would be classified as a paranoid schizophrenic patient. When she came to the clinic, she had been sick for many years and she sometimes had had states of excitement. The last state of excitement was related to the reports about Mexico, that the Catholic Church is persecuted there. She smelt corpses being burned in her house. She refused food and became very excited. In the clinic she very soon developed a rather close relation to me. A similar close relation had existed before she came into the clinic between her and the priest. I wish only to make some remarks about the types of her transference. The patient had had the custom of writing down whatever occurred in her life. She often had visions which were more or less vivid. I am not quite sure whether these visions were real hallucinations. I have the opinion that she had trained herself to provoke vivid optic images, and she very often has said that all of these pictures are substitutes for her prayers.

In addition to this she sometimes has heard voices. In these hallucinations, she saw God, the Father, touch her genitals and then He touched her head with his head. One of the next visions was as follows: "*In the evening, I saw myself kissed by Dr. Schilder as a sick child or as a little sister and he put the fingers of his right hand before my mouth.*" This is another hallucination of the same type. It is interesting that the patient produced the association that she always wanted to be hugged and kissed as a child. The finger before her mouth has the following significance: The patient developed very queer ideas about eating. She has had the idea that the world is changed according to what she eats, and she had the opinion that there would be bad weather if she ate too much potato and if she ate dates then there would be nice warm weather. She had a special disgust for meat and has always had the feeling that it was a special sin to eat meat. Such a sinful meal was connected with the death of some persons. The finger before her mouth means something quite similar to the finger of God on her genitals. She does not make a very great distinction between mouth and genitals; nor between genitals and anus. The patient had the following vision: *There was a doctor for animals and this man took a chicken and he put something which was very sharp into the anus of this chicken in order to provoke better weather.* This vision of the patient has a very close relation to some other visions she did not have about the chicken, but did have about herself. Sometimes she speaks about the physician, sometimes about God himself. Then the patient continues, "At noon I saw God the Father, or Christ consoling me!" All these ideas of transference are in a very close relation to her religious attitude, which is partly an attitude towards the priest, partly an attitude towards God and Christ.

On another day the patient had the following vision. *She saw me at her right looking into a book and kissing her head and we put our heads together.* She compares this with the play of innocent lambs who are playing together, but finally behind this there appeared a symbolization of a close sexual relation of a partly sadistic type. In another vision she saw me taking her hair and kissing her. At the same time she got the hallucination that I tried to creep into her but she excuses that and she says "maybe that is more from a medical point of view." But she says that she feels sexually excited and would like to prevent that. She has heard voices that I wished to go into her genitals, maybe in order to cure her hemorrhoids. (This is again the close relation between vaginal and anal fantasies.) She believed this in order that she could perhaps become completely well.

I think this suffices to show in what way this transference of a very primitive type takes place. It is mixed with anal wishes and anal tendencies and anal fancies, and is also partly of a more magic type. One can indeed work with such a patient to a certain degree, but it is very difficult to make use of such a transference in a psychoanalytic way.

I have also had the opportunity to analyze a schizophrenic patient during intervals when he was completely free, and there I got the transference; but this transference was also mixed with those primitive fancies and ideas that I have just mentioned. This patient once got really frightened in the analytic hour (he was completely in order when I analyzed him), that I would make a homosexual attack on him and would force him to anal intercourse.

If we analyze a neurotic or a healthy person we, of course, get the primitive types of transference also and the anal phase in the transference has to come out as well as the sadistic features. The great difference between the psychotic, the neurotic and the healthy person does not consist in the fact that the psychic contents as such are different. On the contrary, they may be identical. The question is on what contents does the accent lie, in which of these complexes does the individual really live. For the patient, this anal-homosexual transference, while in the remission, had not the same significance as it would have had for him during the psychosis. In spite of his fear, he did not take these homosexual fancies seriously with his whole personality as a schizophrenic would do. It is not the content which is characteristic, but rather it is characteristic in what way a special content is lived in relation to other contents. Primitive transference has to come out in every deep analysis. But the person who is not psychotic will not live it out actually.

It is also necessary to study the transference of a patient who is in stupor. Here narcissism plays a greater rôle but I do not believe that there is any schizophrenic patient who has an *absolute* lack of the capacity for transference. We cannot believe that there are no affective relations to the world; only these relations are insufficient. But the insufficiency is very different in different cases. In the stupors we have the lowest degree of transference capacity we can imagine. We can say that the negativistic attitude also belongs in some way to the very primitive negative transference group. Quite in the same way, the so-called automatism to orders belongs in some way to a very primitive level of undifferentiated attitude towards the world; an attitude towards the world which again comes out in the type of transference especially. We can also say that in every such case the type of transference will be very significant for the whole attitude toward reality and in every case of schizophrenia, we have to study the type of his attitude. Transference is, therefore, the first barometer for the degree of regression.

CHAPTER X

IMPULSE (ANTRIEB), POSTURAL AND RIGHTING REFLEXES IN RELATION TO HYPER-KINETIC STATES

Before I continue the theoretic discussion, I wish to consider with you another patient, McL. This is a man about twenty-five years old. He was always a dreamer, and did not fit well into his world as an office worker. Therefore, he left it and became a sailor, in some way with the idea in the background that he might not only be a sailor, but also a writer, a novelist. Once when he was in Bordeaux, he suddenly developed a state of excitement and he also came into the hospital here in a somewhat similar excited state. The following features were in evidence. Sometimes he turned by himself round his own axis. By this, he said, a change takes place in the world and he turns the world upside down. This peculiar motor activity has continued. Whenever asked to turn around he has the feeling, that when he turns around intentionally it will have some great influence on the world. Every motion of his has great importance for what is going on in the world. When he gets dizzy, others also get dizzy, he says. It is of interest that the patient almost always looks up and turns his head back and sometimes is almost in danger of falling backwards.

When examined as to postures and attitudes the following features were remarkable. When he stretched his hands forward, they came into divergence very quickly. When one turned his head to one side he very often turned his body in the same direction and he came into this movement turning around his own axis, and his movements grew quicker and quicker. Sometimes he resisted a passive movement in a given direction, turned his head in the opposite direction and began to turn in the opposite direction from that in which the experimenter tried to turn his head. One can, of course, say when one observes such a phenomenon that we deal with a patient who has some delusions and is acting according to this delusional thinking. But some other things were rather remarkable in this connection. The patient sometimes gave rather good answers, said that Christ had come again, that it is nonsense to bury dead people, that he would come to them and so on. But sometimes connection with him is completely lost. Then he will not speak for a while. Suddenly he will start shouting several short sentences, mostly commands, in a very loud voice. Generally, the patient has had the tendency to show too much push, too many movements. I do not believe that these hyperkinetic states can be interpreted merely as reactions to delusions. This type of motility belongs to a more primitive level. Of course I do not believe that there is any motility which has nothing at all to do with psychic elements, but the psychic elements of a conscious delusion belong to a rather high level, and this impulse of turning round his own axis belongs to a rather deep level, a level which we can understand better from a physiological point of view.

If a normal person stretches his arms parellel to each other with eyes closed there is a tendency to divergence of the arms. This tendency to divergence belongs to a very primitive motor apparatus which has its center in the medulla oblongata, and in the midbrain; an apparatus the function of which is that of maintaining posture. The position of parallel forward extension of the arms is an artificial position. The natural position of the outstretched arms is one of a deviation of 45–60 degrees from the parallel position. If I order a person to stretch the arms in such a way no movement will take place. In catatonic patients such primitive tendencies to go back to the more convenient postures are increased. The turning around one's own axis can be understood in a similar way. When a normal person turns his head actively and passively to the right side then the trunk and the arms deviate in the same direction. There usually is also a difference in the height of the arms; the arm to which the chin is directed usually goes a little higher than the other one.

These movements of normal persons have also to do with medullary and midbrain mechanisms. We know that in the decerebrate animal, some of these reactions show in a very clear way. Others can only be observed in animals, in whom the nucleus ruber is preserved. We have to do with activities which belong to the postural and righting reflexes. There is a great system for maintaining posture. It begins in the medulla oblongata and goes from the medulla oblongata at least to the nucleus ruber. Magnus and his co-workers have differentiated the different centers. The center for the neck-righting reflexes lies in the anterior parts of the pons region. Most of the other righting reflexes, especially the labyrinthine ones have their centers in the nucleus ruber. The turning around the longitudinal axis is based on the centers of the righting reflexes. The postural and righting reactions, as they appear in normal individuals, are not due to the primitive centers only. There are many psychic influences which are in connection with them. But not only the psychic influence brings with it a change of these centers, there are cerebellar, cortical and perhaps strio-pallidal influences which change the function of these primary centers. For these reactions of normal persons there is at least the same basis as in the reactions we may find in experimental work in animals. What we have observed in this case is certainly typical for hyperkinetic states. With Hoff, I have observed about ten hyperkinetic schizophrenics who showed the same increased tendency to special postural and righting reflexes. These primitive centers of posture are in special action in cases of hyperkinesis of this type. Of course, it is very difficult to say whether these centers as such do not function in the right way, and whether they are more excitable than they are in the normal person. It may be that these many influences which go from the psychic life, or anatomically speaking, from a special part of the cortical region and of others cortical and extracortical to these primitive centers are diminished or increased. I personally am inclined to believe that we have to reckon with changes in the primary postural apparatus of the brain as well as in the secondary.

We have looked at this phenomenon at first from the point of view of physiology, but we must consider that many facts that occur in the physiology of the brain must also have a psychological aspect. We could, for instance, say that this patient acts like a child; children have much stronger postural and righting reflexes than the adult. Schaltenbrand, whom I do not follow in this point, believes that the neck-righting reflex, this turning around of the trunks and arms according to the position of the head, generally disappears when the child is three or four years old. I personally believe that this righting reflex can be demonstrated also in normal older patients but to a lesser degree. But at any rate, we have the right of supposing that some childish elements also enter into these movements. This tendency of turning around one's own axis reminds one in many ways of childish play. They enjoy the sensation they can get out of their muscles and their nervus vestibularis, the nervus vestibularis being such an important part in the different postural activities. But these remarks about children cannot blind us to the possibility that a hyperkinesis like that of our patient is much more primitive than the movement of childish play; we deal with still more primitive tendencies to movement. Could we call them narcissistic? But there again, from the pure theoretical point of view we find a considerable difficulty. These very primitive movements in the righting reflexes are not without aim. This aim is partly in the outward world. The term narcissism is justified only if we abandon the classical analytic formulation that in narcissism there is no outward object at all. There are many other organic impulses which show in encephalitic cases, in chorea. They need a special psychological theory. We cannot give it at the present time.

The short sentences without logical connection have their origin in the increased motor impulses also. I give an instance of the way in which he talks: "I don't rub the world. Don't pay any attention to it. I made Coolidge president. They asked me to. I am ruling all the world above and below. This world is no more than a prick to me. Issue an order to the King of Norway not to use any toothbrushes, never use a toothbrush any more. (shouting) I want that order given and when you eat potatoes peel them with your nails, never use a knife, because I judge them people as imbeciles . . . never use a toothbrush, never use pepsodent, we never use any toothpaste. Western Union Telegraph Company." He is asked how much is three times 50 and he repeats it several times "3 times 50 is 250"; when beginning this he repeats it as often as he repeats the turning around his own axis. Then he shouts in an enumerating way: George of England, Emperor of Japan, Dean of Oxford, etc. Gives again short orders in a loud voice. Thus in speech also, we have therefore increased impulses in our patient. Perseveration occurs when on the one hand there is impulse, on the other no new material. The enumerations too are based on a slow or mechanical progress of thought in connection with a rather strong impulse. Whereas it is possible to point to the physiological background of the turning around the axis and the tendency to divergence, it is far more difficult to find out what the apparatus may be which is involved in this speech trouble. Certainly there is a change in the impulses (Antrieb). One of the centers for those impulses is the striopallidal system. But there is the change in the whole attitude of the patient, i.e., in his magic-narcissistic attitudes toward the world. Attitudes have to do with perceptions and with cortical activities. In the speech troubles, the cortical activities also play an important part. Certainly the turning around the longitudinal axis as well as the speech are active voluntary movements. Still they are partly determined by what is going on in the " deeper " centers.

The differences between the voluntary and the involuntary movements are not so great as they seem to be from a purely formalistic point of view. Experience with the encephalitic shows that the voluntary action is insufficient if there is not at the same time the subcortical help. Whenever there is an increased impulse (Antrieb) of the subcortical type, the patients make too many movements of a more or less voluntary type. They walk around, make all sorts of queer movements, turn around in bed, get up, lie down again. They make movements anxious persons would perform, without being anxious. There is an increased impulse which determines seemingly instinctive movements but without emotion. But the acute cases which one has observed in the great epidemic of 1920 had also sometimes the tendency of speaking more rapidly than they used to. In chronically diseased children, we find also increased motor impulses and these increased motor impulses by and by influence the active voluntary movements. These children are always concerned with something, take it, drop it, tear it, ruin it; they run around, talk, spit. There is constant coöperation between the activities coming from the lower levels of the central nervous system. And we can never understand active movements if we do not reckon with these impulses coming from a lower level of activity which influence the " voluntary movements." There is no doubt that every voluntary tendency brings the subcortical apparatus into action. When we wish, for instance, to speak quickly, we also mobilize certainly subcortical apparatuses. When the conscious impulse is not helped in a sufficient way by the subcortical apparatus, stammering appears. With Gerstmann, I have observed a postencephalitic patient who, when speaking, increased the speed of her speech more and more. The voluntary tendency of speaking got its speed by the increased subcortical impulse.

The apparatus for the impulses is spread over the whole brain and has many foci. One of them lies in the frontal lobe. Some frontal lobe lesions provoke an increased activity. The patients cross their legs, change their position again, hit their thighs, make automatic movements. In the greater part of these cases one finds a marked akinesia. It is connected with psychic indifference. Very likely we deal with a " very psychic " center of impulses. But there is another cortical apparatus of impulse.

It is affected in motor aphasic cases. We know that the motor aphasic patient usually has little impulse to speak. It is certainly not the difficulty in articulation only, which makes him check his impulses. They mostly also sit quietly. In sensory aphasia, we find quite the opposite. I stress the fact that the sensory aphasic patient has not only a hypermotility concerning speech. He not only speaks too much, he also clings too much to other persons who are around him. This is a distinct proof of a cortical activity. It is remarkable that the mood also is changed with those impulses. The motor aphasic is mostly peevish, the sensory friendly and optimistic. He has acquired with an organic lesion a good "transference" to other persons. These cortical activities have certainly to do with the psychic life; they are at least near and intermixed with what we call psychic. At least they have communications with the purely psychic sphere. But, of course, the cortex also influences deeper centers of activity. We know, for instance, that a lesion of the parieto-occipital lobe frees the righting impulses, especially the impulses of turning around the longitudinal axis. Hoff and I have described such cases; something similar was to be seen in a case I observed with Oedegaard in what may have been parietal lobe tumor. According to Dejerine there exists an anatomical connection between the parieto-occipital lobe and the nucleus ruber. Von Monakow denies it but it is certain that the parieto-occipital lobe has connection with the centers of postural and righting reflexes whatever the anatomical paths may be. In some of these cases, a passive movement of the arm induces an "induced movement" of the head, of the trunk. Every passive movement of a limb induces other movements especially of the same side of the body. These are the cortical apparatuses of impulses. Of course, the whole psychic state integrates these activities. These apparatuses are not isolated from the "purely psychic" sphere.

There are important subcortical sources of impulses which are in connection with the striopallidal-substantia nigra system. After the excellent investigations of Wilson and the Vogts, there was the tendency, especially in Germany, to attribute as many functions as possible to the system of the striopallidum. At present, the contrary tendencies exist. Wilson himself denies that the striopallidal system has to do with anything else than with tone and tremor. He denies its relation to impulses. Magnus and Rademaker, according to their experiments on animals, deny even the relation to muscle tone. The experimentalists deny also the importance of the substantia nigra which clinical facts seem to suggest. When we discuss the problem of subcortical activities, we should never forget that there are enormous possibilities of compensation in the subcortical motor system. A lesion of one side will, therefore, be very often compensated and even in a lesion of both sides compensation will be possible. Also the cerebellar system will take part in this compensation. In the first neurological paper I published, I showed how often a crossed lesion of the cerebellum—and the striopallidum provokes choreic and athetotic symptoms. My personal opinion is that we are justified in supposing that the striopallidal-substantia nigra system is one of the most important sources of impulse. The many troubles of impulses in postencephalitic cases I have mentioned point in this direction. Two children with postencephalitic hyperkinesis came to autopsy. In both a lesion of the substantia nigra was found, only in the one, there were slight damages in the cortical region too, in the other, the cortical region was free. (A. Meyer, Bonn.)

Of course the postural and righting reflex apparatus need activities too. In the righting reflex, the animal or the human being tries to get back to its former position. This is an activity of even a lower type than the activities in connection with the striopallidal-substantia nigra system. Of course, even these activities have different levels. The impulses of children above mentioned are on a rather high level. The akinesia of a parkinson patient is an akinesia in centers which are rather far from the psychic influences.

Of late years, Kleist and his co-worker, Merzbach, have ventured the hypothesis that the pallidum internum has to do with the mass movements whereas the putamen and caudatum, substantia nigra and the pallidum externum have to do with finer automatisms. The highest automatisms and impulses, according to Merzbach, are localized in the caudatum and the pallidum externum. The lesion of those is according to his opinion responsible for flexibilitas cerea and pseudo-flexibilitas. These opinions are as yet rather hypothetical. Merzbach brings the caudatum in connection with the iterations especially of speech. Of course, all these activities coöperate. Very likely there never is one of those apparatuses alone in function, but all of them together. It is not a single sound, but a melody. In this connection it is worth while to imagine what is going on during a *hypnosis*. There is the psychic influence of the hypnotizer. This influence must have some cortical connection. But as soon as the sleep and akinesis begins the akinesis progresses to lower centers. Spiegel and Goldbloom have proved that in animals, hypnosis is possible as long as the nucleus ruber is preserved. In animals, the moment hypnosis occurs, primitive postural reflexes come in. In man, hypnotized individuals make many little movements, a sign of increased subcortical activity, before they fall asleep. Quite in the same way, normal sleep goes on. At first there must be the sleeping wish which is based on the whole life situation (partly cortical), then the sleep progresses to the deeper centers of activity and into akinesis. It is remarkable in this respect that in some animals (also in man), righting reflexes are absent during sleep.

Hyperactivity and hypoactivity float very often from one center of the impulse to the other, they are in connection with one another. And in any single case we have to reckon with all these centers spoken of. We know that many imbecile persons cannot check their neck reflex. Whenever you turn their head to the side, these imbeciles have to follow with the trunk. Very likely if there are fewer general inhibitions, there will also be an increased righting reflex. Parker published a case of acute cocaine intoxication with increased impulses. When a patient is acutely intoxicated with cocaine he becomes very fidgety and cannot stand quietly a moment. He always moves around and has at the same time little movements which are like, but not identical with, choreic movements. They are like the movements of impatient persons. This picture of a general restlessness is in connection with higher impulses. But Parker's patient had not only this general restlessness, she also had choreic movements as well as impulses of a lower type. She also had increased righting and postural activities. I suppose it may be that the cocaine had an immediate influence on the centers for the righting reflex, and also on the other centers of activity.

All the apparatuses about which I have spoken have also connections with each other; they are not isolated. Overactivity and increased impulses have to do with several apparatuses in the brain and whenever there is an increased tendency to movement in one apparatus, it is probable that something of this overactivity will flow also to the other associated apparatuses. I have mostly spoken of hyperactivity but hypoactivity follows similar laws and is based on the same apparatuses. I have mentioned, therefore, akinetic hypnosis.

We shall have opportunity to speak more about these states of akinesia when discussing such cases. I wish to return to our particular case McL. In this case we have very likely a primarily increased activity of the postural and righting reflexes but there is also some general cortical hyperexcitability. This patient has not only motor symptoms of divergency and turning around, but has also a peculiar type of shouting and answering. We shall, therefore, now study these symptoms.

The patient sometimes speaks in a rather orderly manner, and he then reports that he is God himself, that he changes the world by his movements, that he turns the world upside down when he turns around. Sometimes he says that dead people are not dead, that he takes them out of their graves, and that he will be burned to death, and that he goes to the sun. But sometimes he begins to shout orders, orders directed to King George or to the Norwegian King. At such times, the single phrases are without any apparent connection. There is a formal change in his thoughts. Which is primary? The formal change in his thoughts or a change in the impulse? Benedek and Schuster and Jelliffe have described patients with encephalitis, who are compelled to shout during such an attack; the intensity of shouting increases more and more. Here, there is an increased impulse which has at least some relation to the striopallidum. But such a change in the motor impulses may bring with it a change in the formal structure of the thoughts. It is at least possible, in our case also, that a primary impulse influences the thoughts. As I have mentioned, the patient shows the phenomenon of perseveration. I asked the patient how much is 3 times 50, and he answered 250, repeated this answer twice and then began to continue by his own impulse to say 3 times 50 is 250, and repeated it at least 20 times. We may say this is a whim. We consider it so, but we must also consider it from the point of view that here is a patient with a motor hyperactivity and this motor hyperactivity causes such repeated reiteration. Iteration and perseveration are not so very different from each other. Iteration is a spontaneous repetition of something which has been done. There cannot be any doubt that such a reiteration can occur in connection with pure organic lesions. I might remind you of the phenomenon of the so-called palilalia as described in cases of encephalitis and striopallidal lesions. Such patients mostly repeat the last words of a sentence several times. Sometimes they repeat them ten or fifteen times. These patients are not psychotic. I do not believe, however, that the iteration of these patients and the iteration of our patient is quite identical. Throughout the whole symptomatology of normal and pathological nervous activities, we see that similar symptoms occur at different levels. What I have reported in the beginning of this lecture about these different apparatus which are in connection with hyperkinesis is especially important also for this problem of reiteration as well as the problem of palilalia and perseveration. It is often difficult to say what such a repetition may mean. In some cases, it is very likely a breaking through of a primary rhythmic function. Many deep organic biological functions have a rhythmic character. This rhythmic basis of the primitive movements shows best in the beating of the heart. Very likely it comes out in the function of walking, and I may remind you of the excellent investigations by Graham Brown who has shown that we cannot understand the walking of animals if we see in them only the answer to proprioceptive and exteroceptive stimuli as Sherrington has believed. We have to assume there is a primary rhythmic action in connection with gait. Animals which are in such a deep narcosis that they do not answer to any stimulus, show rhythmic movements as if they were walking.

The scratch reflex of dogs is also rhythmic. This reflex has to do with very primitive activities of the spinal cord and is to be found also in the so-called spinal preparation of the dog.

The rhythmic function is also primary to the nerve centers and to the life process in general, but there are other sources of rhythm. There is the phenomenon of stuttering and stammering. In most of those cases, we shall find some psychogenetic inhibition which creates a tonic locking. The stammerer usually tries to overcome this feeling of inferiority by increased speed in speaking. When there is no material and articulation the blocking sets in. The individual tries to break through his tonic inhibition and if he does not succeed he has to begin several times and to repeat. In this connection the rhythm, the clonic stuttering, means that at the first attempt the individual was not able to break through. What one observes in stammering and stuttering on the basis of a neurosis, one observes also in encephalitic cases. There are seemingly two activities interfering, one which drives forward and one which hinders. By this interference of impulses, we derive these phenomena of stuttering and stammering.

We come to the very important general formulation: The activities of different levels can interfere with one another. When on the highest level, an activity is checked, whereas on the deeper level the activity goes on, then we shall find phenomena like that of stammering and stuttering. I have observed (with E. Pollak) a very interesting organic case from this point of view. It was a patient whose illness began with stammering. At the same time, she began to be a little slower in her movements, and marked akinesis finally took place. She tried to speak, but her articulation grew worse and worse, and finally she spoke in such a way that she began with one syllable and repeated that syllable but could not continue. The higher activities were still present in spite of the lack of articulation and the possibility of trying; so she began herself to repeat one syllable, but the syllable became more and more unclear and finally her speaking consisted of some rhythmical sounds which were in a rather close relation to the answer she wanted to give. An interesting type of cortical encephalitis was found at autopsy. Very likely we had to deal with an atypical encephalitis especially of the second and third frontal gyrus. The lesions in the striopallidal system were not very well marked. The interference of the different impulses had provoked all the difficulties about which I have spoken. We also have to reckon not only with the fact that what we call impulses go on in different levels of activities, but we have also to realize that impulses in different levels may interfere with each other. If one has very much to say and the articulation does not follow, rhythmic stammering, stuttering results. Rhythm is often a sign of incomplete satisfaction. Therefore, the repetition. I may mention that the patient had micrographia in connection with the lack of impulses. Gerstmann and I have observed micrographia in cases of sensory aphasia and have interpreted this fact as a tendency to write with increased speed which is not helped sufficiently by the lower automatized impulses. The phenomenon of iteration in the patient, McL., can also be considered as a breaking through of the rhythmic tendency in the nervous system, but we can also say that an increased impulse of speaking which shows also in the sudden outbreak of shouting, has no material. His mind does not act quickly enough, and therefore he is compelled to iterate the same phrase very often.

These are the possibilities of interpretation. One does not exclude the other. When the patient sometimes stops speaking, we deal partly with a psychological phenomenon. Perhaps the patient is too strongly interested in his ideas and therefore has not time to answer. That would be the phenomenon of the inhibition, called blocking, which is so well known in schizophrenic cases. In such a case with so many motor symptoms, we must reckon with the possibility that the blocking is partly due to the fact that motor activities are not always at the patient's disposal. There may be a changing akinesis concerning speech also, which could be compared with the akinesis of a stuporous patient. The akinesis would be due to the absence of primitive impulses. One might say that the psy-

POSTURAL AND RIGHTING REFLEXES

chological and the physiological interpretation are identical. I do not believe so because the wish not to speak belongs to a higher level than the impossibility of speaking in connection with the lack of impulses. In every psychic phenomenon, we have to ask on what level of integration does it lie and how far the psychic life on the higher levels may be involved in it. There is the conscious wish not to speak; there are instinctive unconscious wishes not to speak, and there are motor inhibitions which can only with difficulty be compared with the wish not to speak. Let us formulate it in another way: Is this a phenomenon which belongs to the same order as the choreic and athetoid movement? Is it something like the general unrest of a patient who has got an intoxication with cocain; who has with this motor restlessness at the same time also the feeling that he is restless, or is this of the same order as the restlessness of a person who is in anxiety for someone else? We have again to realize that the reality is more complicated than such an antithesis. The increased impulse of lower levels will provoke wishes and tendencies in the higher sphere.

We know that our patient, McL., had the opinion that he could change the world by his movements. And he gave us a nice performance when he made movements with his whole-body assuring us that these movements produce a change in the position of the universe. This idea that he can change the universe has to do with his megalomanic wishes. We are not in any doubt that there is a narcissistic wish behind that and that the life experiences and the regressions are responsible for its particular form. Of course, such a wish may have an influence on the centers of lower activity. But that is only one possibility. There is also a hyperexcitability of the postural and righting reflexes, a special state in the motor apparatus at a lower level. This motor state would bring with it special ideas of the patient. In many of the cases with similar motor phenomena, especially increased divergency, I have found the idea that they are Christ, and that they are on the crucifix. It is probable that the motor postural activity has determined the choice of this special delusion. The psychic life determines the motility and the motility determines the single delusion. We shall not understand these patients if we do not have the conception that the motor state finds its reflection in what is going on in the psychic attitude of the patient. The patient's idea that he can turn the world upside down is in connection with changes in his righting reflexes. These reflexes have the task of bringing the different parts of the body into proper

relation and also of orienting us towards gravity. Some of the righting reflexes—I cannot speak about them in detail—are reflexes whch
orient our head and body in space towards gravity. The otoliths
especially are receptors for gravity and they make an answer to
gravity possible. McL.'s delusion that the world turns upside down
belongs immediately to the group of delusions which reflect a motor
state. One of the righting reflexes I have also often observed in
catatonic patients—I have made these researches together with
Hoff—consists in the fact that when one turns a patient's head backward, the whole body begins to turn backward too in a very exaggerated way. Our patient's opinion that he will go up to the sun may
be related to such a primitive postural reflex. Of course the motor
state alone would never determine the delusions. They are shaped
by the life experience and by the psychic factors. Righting reflexes,
for instance, have been found in an interesting case of Gamper's; a
child who was born without cortex and without optic thalamus. It
had the brainstem only. Gamper observed this child for about three
months. In this child, the first basal part spared was the nucleus
ruber and it still had postural and righting reflexes. We have also
reason to say that the primary centers for the righting reflexes belong
to the phylogenetically old part of the brain. We should expect that
such primitive motility would be connected with a primitive delusion;
therefore I stress the narcissistic type in the thoughts of our patient.

Our patient has the opinion that his movements have a magic influence on the whole world; he also had the idea that he could influence
the results of races and that he could cause some persons to make
much money by betting in races. We come to the idea that very likely
the narcissistic stage of mind has close connections with primitive
motility.

I think also that it is not by chance that the patient has the feeling
that by turning around his own axis he can influence the whole world.
One sees that the psychic interpretation and the interpretation from
the point of view of brain pathology fit each other rather well. The
question again arises, how is it that the patient has gone back to such
a primitive stage of psychic life as well as of motility? I remind
you of the statement that the patient has always been a dreamer, that
he became a sailor with the idea he might become a writer like
O'Neill, Conrad and Jack London. What has happened was again
the difficulty in adaptation to the task which he had as a person at
the age of twenty-three, namely, the task of finding some sex adaptation and some adaptation to special work. We do not know very

much about him. Very likely the failure in the actual task has made him come back to a more primitive stage and to find satisfaction in the narcissistic stage, which he could not find in his actual life.

You see that the scheme we have made use of for the patient L.R. can also be made use of in this patient. But what are the events of his childhood which throw the righting reflex apparatus into a state of hyperexcitability? We cannot say that. And what is the difference between the regression of L.R. and of McL.? That is again the great question. Psychoanalytically we would speak in both cases of a regression to the narcissistic level. In McL. the narcissistic regression involves a greater part of the personality and that is the point I have stressed already in the previous lecture that we have always to consider how great a part of the personality is involved in regression. If the whole personality is in regression then we shall expect that such a patient will not have any adequate conversation with us. Such a patient will be in a more or less complete stupor. Only if a partial regression occurs will be possible that as for L.R. we can speak with the patient. We can get at least some degree of transference and therefore we have always to know how complete the regression is. But the narcissistic stage has also different levels. Very likely there is a deeper regression in a patient in whom the apparatus of motility is more or less involved. There are some subdivisions of this narcissistic level. I personally would be inclined to say that the regression in the case of L.R. is not so deep as the regression in the case of McL. But I confess that it is very difficult to prove such an opinion.

The regression to the narcissistic level is also in connection with changes in the emotions and whenever we find a regression we shall find changes in the emotions also. Of course the emotions are not only dependent on the deepest level which is reached but are also dependent on other points of fixation. In the case of L.R. we find a point of fixation in homosexuality. These differences of fixation may partly be responsible for the difference in the varying pictures of schizophrenia. We have also to say that in the schizophrenic cases we have to consider the actual factors, the actual difficulty. We have to consider the point of fixation, but not only the point of fixation at the narcissistic level but also the points of fixation which are at other levels, for instance, in the case of L.R. in the homosexual sphere. Besides that we have to consider whether the regression takes place with a great part of the personality or only with a smaller part of the personality. And further we have to answer the question whether there are not different levels of narcissistic points of fixation and whether motor phenomena of the type I have described do not belong to a deeper level of narcissism. Finally we have to say that the emotions will be in close relation to the different points of fixation. We should ask also in every case what has remained of the previous personality. We have to ask about the Ideal of Ego in such patients. I have stressed already regarding the case of L.R. that a great part of her Ideal Ego is preserved. In the case of McL. also a part of the Ideal Ego has been preserved which drives him to reality, otherwise he would not communicate at all with us. He would not be interested in procuring money for other persons. We also have to reckon with the fact that in such a case as McL. there is never a complete destruction of his Ideal Ego and of the relations to the reality. Moreover, in such a case not the whole personality is on the way to regression.

CHAPTER XI

AKINETIC STATES, ON STUPOR AND ON NEGATIVISM

In the case McL. I have discussed, there are also increased impulses (Antrieb) partly of a higher level (psychic), partly of a lower level (righting and postural reflexes). What I have observed in this case can be observed in other cases too. There is, for instance, the boy Rub. (seventeen years old) with a general restlessness; he mostly walks around when he is not sleeping; he is in a state of over-activity. At the same time he speaks a great deal. What he says is not well connected. There is some degree of incoherence. When I order him to stretch out his arms, he, too, shows a marked degree of divergence of the arms. When I turn his head in a passive way, his trunk follows in an exaggerated way the turning of the head. The patient shows vivid grimaces and is always moving his arms and hands also. I do not wish to go into the details of his history. I wish only to say that his psychosis began in connection with some actual difficulties. He was always peculiar as a child; was boisterous with ideas of grandeur already before the psychosis set in. He was very likely attacked homosexually by his music teacher before the psychosis came on. The psychosis has also to be considered as a regression to a more primitive motility of the hyperkinetic type. We have to consider the grimaces from a similar point of view. In such a case they are not in very close relation to the emotions. We have not discussed as yet the important part that the optic thalamus plays in primitive motility. It is a station which has a great importance for the emotions and their expression. Head supposed that feeling tone is added to perception in the optic thalamus. This conception is too mechanistic. But certainly in the optic thalamus an integration of sensory impulses takes place. But this integration immediately influences the apparatus of the pallidum and putamen. Besides this, cortical activities of emotion are transferred to the optic thalamus and from there to the striopallidal system, which, according to most inves-tigations, has no direct relation to the cortex (with the exception of the pallidum). Whenever there is a change in the expression of emotions we have the right to suppose that thalamic activities are changed. If we find such a motor picture as in our patient, there is not only one apparatus of the motility changed; one might say we are not justified to consider these phenomena from a neurological point of view; they are only the expression of a dissociation of the personality. Of course, the motor phenomena as well are a dissociation of the personality. These different motor tendencies in the hyperkinesis do not fit in with the contents of what he is saying. But this hyperkinesis in connection with a psychic dissociation makes the different motor apparatuses of the brain and the emotional part of motility (optic thalamus) function in a changed way. The melody of the operation of these somatic apparatuses is changed. We shall discuss now from a similar point of view akinetic states of motility.

I shall start with a little remark concerning our first patient L.R. She does not show any signs of motor troubles in the usual sense, but there is not only her emotional indifference but also an indifference in her attitude, in her facial expression, and in the way she speaks. This is due to her regression to the narcissistic stage. She is living in the sphere of this magic influence and this means at the same time a change in her activities. It is only a higher degree of the same trouble that we see in the case of McL. when he suddenly stops speaking for a while and does not show any signs of activity. The blocking has to do with the state of narcissism, with the going back to more primitive stages. Whenever a patient gets interested in these deeper lying fancies there will be some lack of activity. We can also see in such a hyperkinetic state as McL. that from time to time there is a lack of activity. But in many of the cases we have a much more complete withdrawing from the world, and then we have before us the type of real stupor. I would say, from the point of view of the psychoanalytic theory, we have to consider that patients in hyperkinesis have no close relations to the world. It has been often observed that the hyperkinetic person does not really act. He always does something but does not come in relation to the world with all his doings. He more or less enjoys his own actions in a very primitive way, but he is not directed towards the world. It is more a pleasure of the movement of his own body and not an action which is directed towards the world. It is a special type of withdrawing from the world living in the activities of one's own body. Yet this conception is too schematic. In the previous remarks I have already pointed to my general idea that after all there is also some aim in very primitive types of movement. Beings of whatever kind have always some tendency, some attitude, towards the world. This world may be a very primitive one. This remark is contrary to the general psychoanalytical opinion that narcissism is a state where objects do not exist at all. It is a basic part of the human organization that there is always an object and a subject. It is only the degree of differentiation which varies. In hyperkinetic narcissistic stages there is a relation to the world but the subject-object relation is still undifferentiated.

The withdrawing from the world shows more clearly in cases of stupor: The patient Cham., now thirty years old, became sick in 1926. At the beginning of his mental troubles he was very uncertain whether he should continue his engagement to a girl or whether he should break with her. After that there developed some neurotic complaints about his stomach. Finally he lost interest in things, gave up his job, complained about his teeth, did not want to eat, became slow in his movements and lazy. Finally he made an attempt to get out of his state, enlisting in the army in order to be forced to work. We deal here with one of those common desires in the beginning of schizophrenia to get rid of the disease, to get closer relations to the world again. From that time he went deeper and deeper into the stupor I wish to describe. As one approaches the patient he has at first a facial expression between astonishment and fear. Every movement one makes in coming nearer to him increases his fear. He withdraws in a very instinctive way. I would stress the fact that the patient when withdrawing does not effect a really efficient withdrawal. It is in some way an incomplete action, a very primitive action. It is interesting that when one threatens the patient with the fist, the withdrawing of the patient and his whole expression and his whole motor attitude do not change very much. It is the same whether you try to shake hands with him or whether you come near his face with a threatening gesture. If now one tries to take hold of his hand, something peculiar takes place. At that very moment he withdraws the hand with rather great force. If one insists sometimes the patient gives in and then you can hold his hand very quietly. But sometimes the patient continues in his resistance against your grip and he develops sometimes a great and strong resistance in the muscles. But still he never begins with a defense which would really be efficient. He will never push you back or pull out his hand and run away. The defense remains in the local sphere. It is not integrated with the whole motility or the whole personality, but it remains a local phenomenon. When one hurts the patient by pinching or hitting with rather great force he will say " Indeed I feel it " when asked, but still his defense reactions remain local ones. He will never push you back, he will never try really to escape. We have a purely local reaction.

On taking him out of bed and drawing him toward me he will resist very strongly in the beginning. From a given moment his resistance stops and I can draw him passively towards me. He is now near to me, suddenly he goes back, he does not remain there, and comes to me again. I try to shake hands with him. I offer him my hand, he withdraws his hand; but suddenly an impulse to give me the hand comes and he brings his hand nearer to mine, always coming a little nearer and withdrawing again, but finally he comes to shake hands with me.

I put his hand in the position in which we examine catalepsy. The patient remains for a while in this position, then he begins to drop the arms, and goes back again to the position I gave him before. The patient does not speak very much. Sometimes he says short phrases. For instance, as I asked him: " Do you feel the pain? " he said, " Of course I feel it." Sometimes he makes some other rather short remarks. He does not eat spontaneously. He must be spoon-fed. There are some other very interesting phenomena. He has queer pupillary reactions. Usually his pupils react, but only when he is quiet. When his muscular resistance begins, the pupillary reaction becomes slighter and disappears completely. The Achilles tendon and the patellar tendon reflexes are absent. Also the reflexes of the arms are absent. We have a patient before us who has withdrawn from reality, but even these patients who have withdrawn from reality have retained some relations to the world. They are not completely narcissistic. There is always some differentiation between world and body. Some relation to other persons still remains, but it is important to know that this relation is not a specialized one. It is a general relation. Towards a friendly gesture he reacts in no other way than to a threatening gesture. He has only one reaction, and this reaction is a reaction of the negativistic type, or not wanting to get into closer relations. This negativistic reaction is not a reaction of the whole personality or of the whole motility, but is a reaction which remains in some way in a localized field, and we come perhaps to the opinion that in primitive states of motility we shall find movements which are less integrated with the whole personality than the movements we find in the more highly developed states. But it would not be right to say there is only negativism. We could say that behind this negativism there is also some positive tendency, or we could say that in the motor movement we can find something we could call ambivalence. The ambivalence shows itself in the way he shakes hands, in the way in which he goes forward with his hands, withdraws, goes forward again, and finally if repeatedly urged shakes hands. In this primitive state of motility the reaction will not only be a more localized one but it will also not be so sure whether the reaction is a reaction against or a reaction toward. His motor tendencies may be something similar to the ambivalence he has shown in the very beginning of the disease. This ambivalence concerned the question whether he should stay in his engagement or break the engagement. Here we come to the important question: is the psychic phenomenon of indecision about the engagement in some way akin to the motor phenomenon we can see here? I would say that they are the same tendencies expressed on different levels. The patient Co. whom I shall discuss later also shows some ambivalent tendencies in her motility. But her motility is not as primitive as the motility of our patient and therefore the relation between motility and emotion is clearer in her case.

If at the beginning of schizophrenia such an ambivalent tendency appears it must have to do with psychic problems and phenomena. The problem of ambivalence is very closely related to the problem of negativism. I may start the discussion by referring to the interesting controversy between Bleuler and Jung about schizophrenic negativism. Bleuler has the opinion that such a negativism is sometimes in connection with the autistic tendency of the individual. On other occasions the negativism may be in connection with the fact that the individual does not get the right orientation about what is going on. Then he speaks about the negativism which is in connection with the "Lebenswunde," the wound received in the life experiences. And finally he mentions that beside other complexes also the sexual complex may provoke the negativism. But Bleuler has the opinion that ambivalence as well as negativism are secondary in comparison to primary troubles of associations which are for him the immediate expression of the organic process of the schizophrenia.

Jung objects to this point of view. He says we have no right to speak of the psychology of something primary which is in immediate connection with a lesion of the brain, and he tries to study the problem of negativism and of ambivalence from the purely psychological point of view. For him there are motives, or as he says complexes, of the patient which make him resistant, ambivalent, negativistic.

Indeed the problem in such a beginning schizophrenic case is what the motives are which make him ambivalent about his engagement.

If one would study a beginning case of this type one would then find that some points of fixation have been revived, *e.g.,* a homosexual one, and that with this homosexual point of fixation also the pleasure of his own body may have been revived: the feeling that he is too good to get in some closer relation with somebody else. We do not know the motives which lead our patient to such a deeply negativistic attitude. His actual problems alone cannot explain this. If there are motives which have created the point of fixation they must have been in a very primitive narcissistic psychic sphere. We cannot find analogy to such a primitive state in the experience of the child because we cannot get any utterances at that stage of development. Of course we can say this motor ambivalence and motor negativism of our patient belong to a similar group as the psychic ambivalence. But it would be wrong to say that we deal with something which is quite the same. We cannot understand the "motor ambivalence" completely. It is only possible to compare it with some psychic manifestations we could observe at the very beginning of the psychosis of our patient. We have to do with a phenomenon which belongs to the deep phases of regression. This can be proved by the coincidence of such a stupor with a phenomenon of the pupils. Catatonic pupillary reactions are indeed very interesting. Emotions have a great influence on them. E. Meyer in Königsberg has shown that sometimes this phenomenon can be provoked by pressure against the abdomen. But other emotions can provoke it also. It can be provoked also by some greater muscular strain. Our patient gets this reaction when he struggles against us. Also in normal people it is sometimes possible to get some changes in the pupillary reflexes by muscular strain (Redlich). The phenomenon occurs also in encephalitic cases. We have before us a phenomenon of the involuntary muscles in close relation to primitive emotion and muscular resistance. The emotions have on the one hand one subcortical station in the optic thalamus but there is another in the gray substance around the third ventricle. A. Westphal, who first described the pupillary reaction in the catatonics, brings them in connection with changes in this place. There is no doubt that these pupillary phenomena have an organic as well as a psychogenic basis.

Are there organic phenomena which are comparable with the phenomenon of the negativism? Kleist has seen them in thalamic lesions and in cases where lesions of the basal nuclei are combined with cortical lesions. Many years ago I observed a choreic case due to an organic lesion. Whenever I ordered the patient to make a movement, a movement in the opposite direction took place. The involuntary impulse of the choreic type went into the antagonists. I have had the opportunity to see among the cases here in the Phipps Clinic an organic case in which marked negativistic tendency in the muscles was obvious. This was the patient Hei., an arteriosclerotic who got suddenly worse seemingly in connection with an apoplexy. He had not only a tendency to grasp whatever he perceived but there was also a well marked sucking reflex. He was restless and tried again and again to drill his finger into the wall with very great force. When he approached his own body he treated it like the wall and drilled his finger with great force against his own body. It was rather difficult to keep him from hurting his own eye. Whenever one attempted to make a passive movement with one of his arms, this arm grew completely stiff in the agonists as well as in the antagonists. It was astonishing that this phenomenon did not take place in passive movements of the head. It was only in connection with the extremities. The patient also pushed his feet with very great force against the wall; sometimes he pressed his body with force against the wall. This patient also showed a very peculiar attitude towards pain. He did not take care at all that he was in danger of hurting his eyes. His grasping reflex sometimes brought his penis into his hands and he grasped it with such a force that he was in real danger of hurting it. When I applied painful stimuli to his arms he did not react at all.

The relation of such a picture to the picture of negativism is rather obvious. Of course there is not a complete identity. One could say that the patient was delirious and his consciousness was not clear when these troubles occurred. Perhaps part of these symptoms were due to his general cortical trouble and not neurologic in the common sense. Yet the greater part of this picture was of a doubtless organic type. His muscular negativism was comparable with the negativistic tendencies of the catatonics. I would also believe that the negativistic tendencies of the catatonics can be partly understood from the point of view of brain pathology. It is astonishing that the organic and the catatonic negativism are usually not spread over the whole body. The first signs of negativism appear in the jaw and in the neck muscles. Jaw and neck muscles are the muscles which are in the closest relation to negativism. That has to do with the fact that the resistance of a normal person in a struggle shows in these muscles first. Also when we resist psychically we stiffen our necks and press our teeth together. We say therefore about an obstinate person, that he has a stiff neck. Maybe we have been too little interested up to recent times in the organic problems of normal psychology. I may add that it is of a great significance to have a stiff neck, and to be headstrong. The position of the head, by way of postural and righting reflexes, influences, as we have stated, the tonus of the whole body. The fact that our sense organs lie to a great part in our head may be partly responsible for this great significance of the head for motility. The tendency to press the teeth together has much to do with the enormous importance of the oral zone. It is a defense mechanism.

We meet the problems of our pathological cases in everyday life also. Language points very often to these important psychological connections. Every psychic attitude must be in connection with the functions of the brain and its apparatus. Very likely we are justified in supposing that the catatonic negativism has to do with the same apparatuses which are affected in the organic cases which show symptoms similar to the negativism. Of course our knowledge about the apparatus is still very incomplete. Kleist claimed at first that the frontal lobe plays an important part in these symptoms. He is inclined now—as I have mentioned—to see the real center in the optic thalamus. Yet he does not deny an influence of the cortex on all these apparatuses which have to do with tonus, automatism, impulse, rigidity and all sorts of choreic and athetotic movements.

Here I may mention the interesting experiments by de Jongh and Schaltenbrand with bulbocapnin. It is possible by injecting bulbocapnin into an animal to get a picture which is like the picture of paralysis agitans. The righting reflexes are absent. That is very likely due to cortical inhibition. When the dose is increased the symptom disappears. Epileptic fits may occur. Instead of the inhibition an irritation has taken place. Here is the proof that there is an important influence of cortical apparatus in akinetic pictures. I may illustrate how far psychic influences involve deeper subcortical apparatuses by an old observation of mine. This was a patient with a senile disorder of gait. He could walk rather freely, but if he should pass between two chairs he could not go on. He stopped and made quick stamping movements with his feet but could not pass. It was surely not a pure psychogenic trouble. He showed some kind of rigidity, not very well marked, and a face without expression. When the patient was lying on the bed he was completely relaxed; he had no hypertonus in his muscles, but at the very moment I brought my hand near his leg he developed a marked plastic tonus of the paralysis agitans type. The tonus-tension resistance apparatus is in very close relation to psychic influences. When there is a psychic regression to a very primitive stage we may expect also changes in the tonus. The organic interpretation does not imply any contradiction of the psychic interpretation. The two interpretations supplement each other. This is also the point of view of Jelliffe in his study on the relation of schizophrenia to epidemic encephalitis. In such a case of stupor as Cham. we deal with a very primitive motility, a state in which strio-pallidal and thalamic brainstem mechanism and some of the more primitive cortical mechanisms prevail. But why the motor melodies are changed we cannot say. These catatonic states are never completely identical with the states we find in gross lesions of the brain. We can only suppose that the same apparatuses are changed in both cases. Very likely in the organic lesions and in the lesions of that type we have a similarity in the apparatuses which are in function or out of function, but very likely the agency which gets the apparatus out of function is different and this agency works in a different way in the purely organic cases and in a case of this type. There exist very close relationships between the dissociation of the motor answers, the motor ambivalence and the primitive psychic life. The way in which our patient behaves toward pain stimuli is especially interesting. He behaves as if it were not the whole personality which reacts to pain. This is a reaction similar to what Stengel and I have observed in a parietal lobe lesion: In these cases of asymbolia for pain the patients show local reactions but not a reaction of the whole personality. They do not appreciate the pain which very likely is perceived. On the basis of an autopsy finding we have assumed that a lesion of the supramarginal gyrus is responsible for this symptom. We have had an opportunity of observing a patient from whom a parietal lobe tumor was removed and in whom the perception of pain was not deranged at all. But this patient showed the same queer motor reactions towards pain we had observed in the cases of asymbolia. We could call that an apraxia for pain. But the term is not quite correct, since the more instinctive mechanisms of defense are impaired. Whatever term we may choose the most important fact is that there are such close relations between phenomena in parietal lobe lesions and phenomena observed in a catatonic case. The parietal lobe is an organ which integrates the single impressions of sensibility of the whole body. The postural scheme of the body has its basis there. Pain stimuli have to be brought in connection with the postural scheme. The postural scheme has also to prepare the motor responses and it has a deep meaning that those parts of the brain which have to do with the postural pattern are on the one hand situated near the place a lesion of which provokes an asymbolia for pain and to those parts a lesion of which provokes apraxia. In the same region Hoff and I assume a center for the postural and righting apparatus.

In these discussions we have stressed that the primitive motor centers in the schizophrenic act in a special way. We should not forget that there are hints that the cortical function is also impaired. It is certainly not possible to understand the neurology of schizophrenia from the subcortical point of view alone.

We have not discussed as yet the absence of the tendon reflexes in this case. According to the experience of Guttmann and J. Haenel absence of kneejerks does not occur so rarely in schizophrenia. I myself have not seen it in other cases and consider therefore the symptom as an atypical one. It may be that it is only an accessory symptom which is in connection with the undernourishment of those patients, but there is the possibility that it is due to a toxic influence of the disease as such. But there are many other types of negativism also; we shall discuss them in connection with the case Co.

CHAPTER XII

MANNERISMS AND EMOTIONS

In the case of Cham. we found dissociation of the different impulses of motility. The positive and the negative impulses do not make a whole and are not integrated with the whole personality. Negativism is in this way a dissociation phenomenon and has very likely to do with the ambivalence which shows not only in every thought but also in every one of our actions. In every movement there are not only antagonistic impulses but we have also to integrate impulses which would go in different directions. The dissociations occur in the different levels. The dissociations I have discussed in the last lecture lie on a rather deep level. I shall discuss to-day a case which also shows a considerable degree of dissociation but on a higher level. In such a case it is easier to study the psychological problem.

The patient Co. whom I shall discuss to-day is now twenty-six years old. The disease began on the first of May; she was depressed, got crying spells, and thought she could not continue her work. On May 14 she expressed the idea she would be unable to take a new position and continue her work. On May 17 while visiting her aunt she asked her mother to accompany her home and told her she had thought of intercourse with her fourteen-year-old cousin, and wanted to leave. The next day she was very excited and said her physician had had intercourse with her and accused the nurse of bringing others for the same purpose.

Such a beginning with an outburst of heterosexuality which does not lead to real heterosexual action is rather typical. It is usually an effort on the part of the patient to hinder total regression. These patients very often then begin to masturbate; sometimes they have manifest heterosexual fantasies. But these are put forward to escape a more primitive perverse sexuality. Masturbation in this case need not mean that the real genital level has been reached. Masturbation can have a different significance. It is an expression for very different psychosexual attitudes. Something which is not in close relation to the genitals can still be expressed by way of masturbation, *e.g.,* sadistic impulses. Masturbation of the schizophrenics has to be considered from such a point of view. That masturbation of the schizophrenic can be autistic is proved by the fact that they are often absolutely careless about the presence of others. They ignore other persons. The heterosexuality our patient displays is a hetero-sexuality of a promiscuous type. Promiscuity usually increases at lower levels of sexuality. The less important the object is the greater the promiscuity. As a rule in perversions promiscuity is greater than in the normal heterosexual relations, and if we find in heterosexuality a great amount of promiscuity from the psychoanalytic point of view we have a suspicion there might be some other tendency behind it, *e.g.*, latent homosexuality. Promiscuity means that we do not really value the love object. What we hear about the patient proves that her sexuality is regressing. The patient also loses interest in hiding her urination and defecation and becomes unclean. There is some parallelism between the attitude toward defecation and urination and towards sex matters. The patient in an autoerotic way not only enjoys her masturbation but also her urination and uncleanliness.

We shall now turn to the description of the motor behavior. When the patient comes in she turns her head towards the wall and it is rather difficult to make her speak and to turn her head back. Schizophrenics very often turn away their heads; they hide their faces when speaking with somebody or let their hair droop over their faces. This expresses autism as well as negativism. Moreover, these phenomena can occur on very different levels. A schizophrenic patient I am now analyzing and who is very well composed and does not show very marked troubles in her formal behavior, usually covers her face during the analysis and turns her face away from me. In other patients of this type this attitude becomes much more manifest. Thus we are not so far from the picture of torticollis. I have observed schizophrenic patients in whom marked torticollis was present. Negativistic or autistic tendencies in these cases also find an expression on very different motor levels. The one motor level is very near to the normal expression of the emotions and the deeper we go the more mannerisms we find, and finally we come to motor expres-sions which are rigid, like attitudes in organic lesions.

This brings us to the problem of mannerisms. Mannerisms are expressions of primitive dissociated emotions. It is very interesting to study our patient from this point of view a little more carefully. When I speak to her she turns her head away but when I give her a short command, " Turn your head back," she obeys. She wishes to go away. When I give her the short command, " Now get up, now take some steps," she obeys and we can say that in connection with these autistic negativistic tendencies there is at the same time an almost increased tendency to obey short commands. Paradoxical as it may sound, automatism to commands is not altogether opposed to negativism of this kind. We have again before us a dissociation not only between the different motor impulses as pure motor impulses, but a dissociation in the motor expression of the emotions. This queer picture of different emotions also comes out in this patient in another way. When one watches the expression on her face it is very difficult to say whether she is crying or whether she is laughing. Some muscles in the face around the eyes give her the expression of laughing whereas the other parts of the face yield a more crying expression. It is a queerly dissociated face. It is a dissociation between the motor expression of the different emotions. What holds for the face also holds for the rest of the body. The face, of course, is that part of the body where expression of the emotions is best seen, but every part of the body has also expressive faculties. We should not be astonished to see in another case that there is a difference between the expression of the face and the expression of the rest of the body. But this patient has in addition another very remarkable symptom. While she is speaking she suddenly begins to mumble something and she makes some movements like sighing. That is a movement which we can consider directly as a tic. The diaphragm is involved in it. The patient complains about the tic-like movement and wishes to be cured of it. The same dissociation which causes the mixture of the emotional expression also provokes this queer tic.

When we are in the field of tics we are in some way on familiar ground. There is a connection between the tics and the bodily apparatus for the expression of involuntary movements. In the so-called neurotic tic, the striopallidal system is also involved. In postencephalitic cases we meet with tics which have a purely organic basis. Identical pictures may occur when we have before us patients who after psychic conflict begin to turn the head away. Very likely in these neurotic cases we have to reckon with some organic disposition to reaction in such a way. We may assume in our case also the organic basis. No doubt there is an ambivalent psychic tendency in our patient, but this ambivalent psychic tendency acts on the apparatuses which have to do with involuntary motility and the apparatuses which have to do with the expression of the emotion. These apparatuses are the striopallidal system and the system of the anterior part of the optic thalamus. The optic thalamus has something to do with the emotions. We do not know how much, but in optic thalamus cases we find that the patients have a special condition of sensibility towards pain. They also experience spontaneous pain. Whenever they get pain this pain is of a terrible strength, and it is very likely that there exists some relation between lesions of the optic thalamus and the emotions. I do not believe as Head believes that a lesion of the optic thalamus can also make pleasure stimuli more pleasant, but I still believe that feeling and emotions have some connection with the optic thalamus. It is certainly only one of the stations which have to be passed before we get a complete feeling towards the situation. According to Nothnagel we find a lack of the expressive movements in the face after thalamic lesions. These patients do not have a palsy of the facial nerve as such but they lose the faculty of making use of the facial nerve for such facial movements as laughing and crying. We would suppose that in this patient the relations between her psychic life and the expression of the psychic life which is partly based on the thalamic apparatus are disturbed, and I would take her as an instance of a trouble in the cortico-thalamic relations in a schizophrenic. In other cases perhaps we have to seek the trouble in the expressions of the emotions somewhere else. In the case of Cham. we find the trouble in the relation between the cortical region and some deeper centers for motility and some deeper centers for the expression of the emotions. According to this difference in the motility we find also differences in the psychic attitudes of our patients. The patient Co. is able to give answers. We can have a conversation with her, in keeping with the fact that her motility is not the motility of a very low level, whereas the patient Cham. has a motility of a very dissociated type and in connection with this very dissociated motility, we find also that it is almost impossible to get in contact with him.

In these discussions I have often emphasized that autism and negativism have relations to each other. Of course, whenever a patient is more interested in himself and gives less interest to other persons he will try to get rid of the relations with other persons. The increased interest in one's own personality will provoke negativism towards others.

We may now return to the psychic symptoms of our patient. The patient very often builds up one pattern and sticks to it and is not able to change it according to the circumstances. For instance for some weeks she has always asked, " I don't want to live. Let me die, give me some possibility to die." She repeats this phrase every day several times, almost always with the same accent and with the same words. It is one of the troubles in her emotional life that she is unable to adapt herself to different situations. She has only one pattern she can make use of. We find something similar in her other troubles of motility. She perseveres in her facial expressions and in the posture of her head. *Perseveration* also has different degrees. Cha. also perseveres in the type of his motor answers. I have made the observation that when I approached him with friendly gestures he withdrew quite in the same way as when I approached in the most threatening way possible. Also McL. shows perseveration. We have perseveration also of very different degrees. In this case Co. the perseveration consists in the sticking to one topic and repeating it always and we come also to the conclusion, especially in connection with perseveration, that all these patients have not only a dissociated motility but they have also lost their ability to adapt themselves in their motility as well as in their emotions. They react to all situations more or less in the same way. This is again a fact which is of great importance.

Of course, it is very difficult to say what such a wish might mean for the patient Co., whether she really wants to die or not. Whenever she says this, she has her queer mixed expression in her face. The mixed expression in the face belongs to her whole psychic attitude and especially to the whole psychic attitude she has always developed towards sex. The patient was practically sexless before she became ill and fulfilled in this respect the ideal of so many parents who by the repressions of their own would like their daughters to be sexless beings until they are married. I do not believe that sexless beings really exist, and whenever we find no manifest tendencies of sexuality in somebody we have to suppose there a very strong tendency to repression. In this respect it is rather interesting that one finds the most innocent girls among those who have hysteria. All the knowledge about sex matters seems to be lacking and it seems as if sex desires had never existed. In hysteria it is rather easy to find out by the analysis that the sexuality behind this seeming lack of sexuality is an enormous one. In cases of schizophrenia it is more difficult to say what is really going on. Is this lack of sexuality already a beginning of the autistic tendencies in the patient? Is this withdrawing a regression to a very early and primitive stage? This is very difficult to say, but there must have certainly been a struggle between the sexual and the asexual tendency. The patient has told two girl friends of hers who are married that she cannot understand why one falls in love and marries. We have, of course, to consider these problems not from the point of view of purely genital relation alone. In all sex relations the question of tenderness and real love plays a very important part. We do not know enough about what is really going on with the patient, but in keeping with our experience in other cases we suppose a violent fight between the different sex tendencies and the repression. The outbreak of the psychosis is in a very close relation with the outbreak of such strong tendencies, whether they are heterosexual ones or of a more primitive type. Whenever we study a patient carefully we find behind the front many impulses in conflict with each other. There is a series of crossing impulses and we have to pass through many layers before we come to the underlying tendencies of the individual. We never know whether something that appears on the surface is the expression of some genuine tendency or the expression of some tendencies of overcompensations of other strivings. Therefore it is rather difficult to say what this outburst of sexuality in our patient means, but what is of importance for us is that in this conflict between the sexual and the asexual there is again a dissociation as in her state of motility. I do not believe that the problem of the motility of these patients and their emotional, especially sexual, problems are very different from each other. You remember, perhaps, that I have also tried to make a connection between the attitude of our patient, Cham., and the fact that in the very beginning of the psychosis he was uncertain whether he should break his engagement or whether he should continue it.

But let us go back to our patient. What may be the meaning of her repeated wish that one should let her die? She brings it forth in some erotic way and it may be that this death wish is in some way a tendency to permit a closer relation to the physician who is to kill her We can see in such repeated phrases an attempt to have at least some primitive relation to the world, which after all remains ambivalent. The patient has actually made utterances of that kind. For some weeks she repeated in a stereotyped way: " I want to go home, let me go away." But she never has made a real effort to get away. Also this "let me go away " may indicate some positive relation. What comes out in this queer expression of her face comes out in some way in every utterance of the patient and we can consider the psychic motives and the expression in the motility from a very similar point of view. We can say the patient is manneristic. She has mannerisms and that is one of the most characteristic symptoms in the motility of schizophrenic patients. These mannerisms are in some way like play. If the psychosis progresses, and if deeper layers become involved, we find the mannerism fixed and the grace of the patients disappears more and more until they become more and more stiff and set. Of course, we could say that the stiffness or the rigidity of the hyperkinetic motilities are also expressions of mannerisms.

It is worth while to study these problems from a more general psychological point of view. If we meet a normal person and if we remark about him, that he behaves in a manneristic way, we mean that he wishes to appear by his attitudes to be a person such as he is not in reality. There is behind every mannerism, some discrepancy between different impulses. It may be that the motility does not obey the more central parts of the personality. Every person who becomes too self-conscious, tends to get into manneristic movements. This problem of the normal finds, in some way, its elaboration in the mannerisms of the schizophrenic. Whenever the motility has not developed enough, then we also get the impression that there is a lack of grace and we also get the impression that there are some mannerisms. It is very interesting from this point of view that Homburger and his coworkers have studied the development of the normal motility in children and have found many relations of this undeveloped motility to the schizophrenic. It takes some time before the children coördinate their movements in the right way. Mannerisms and lack of grace are common when there are special aims which the motility cannot fulfill. At the time of puberty, this dissociation between the movements and their aims plays a very important part. In this rush of development, the psychic and the motor development do not always progress at the same pace and then we shall find mannerisms.

Manneristic attitudes will often be connected with another phenomenon which also is of interest for the psychology of dementia praecox, and especially for its motor troubles. This is the attitude of play acting. The schizophrenic will show some poses and the attitudes of a comedian. The phenomenon is to be found in the so-called normal too when he tries to overcompensate feelings of uncertainty. The beginning schizophrenic acts in an exaggerated way.

I may quote in this connection the patient, Sess., twenty years old. She has always had an expression which is in some way exaggerated. It is set as if she were playing a tragic or a comic part. Usually, when observed, she plays the part of the girl who is very proud and sneeringly sends her lover away. But all her movements are exaggerated, and sometimes she remains in a set posture as if she were frozen in it. The play-acting is very closely connected with the mannerisms, and we could say that play-acting and emotion, *i.e.,* making something voluntary of what should be involuntary, is the first stage of mannerism. The beginning schizophrenic knows that he acts. He acts sometimes craziness, insanity, not knowing that his unconscious is earnest in what he believes to be play. The development of the motility of the child is certainly a development of coördination between the different motor apparatuses. The striopallidal system, the thalamus, the corpus subthalamicum, the cerebellar system and the rubral system play as important a part as the motor apparatus of the cortex. Some children move in such a manner that it is difficult to distinguish their motility from that of a patient who is affected with chorea minor. It is remarkable in this respect that chorea is indeed a disease which occurs mostly in children. Also the choreic and the athetotic movements in post-hemiplegic cases are much more common in those who had brain lesions in childhood. I stress those facts because I do not think that the problem of organic pathology is so different from the problems of psychology with which we deal. I may immediately add that one of the cases I shall discuss in the next hour, that is the case of Mrs. Hask., had chorea in her childhood, and it is known that not only patients with catatonic troubles but also their relations, are relatively often affected with chorea or choreiform troubles. A mannerism is also a sign of a motor dissociation. If one cries and laughs at the same time, the result will be a manneristic expression of the face as one sees in this case. The dissociation is also the most characteristic trait in all those troubles. But the dissociation is of a different degree. We find in Sess., a dissociation which is rather easily understood from a psychological point of view, and which is not so very different from what we can understand with our every-day psychology. We found in Co., a dissociation which goes deeper and makes us think of a relation to a specially deep lying center in the thalamic region. We find in other cases that dissociation goes a step deeper, as in the case of Cha., cases which give the impression that there might be a connection with still more primitive centers. We find all kinds of dissociation and behind them the tendencies of negativism, which again are of a very different type. The negativism of the patient, Sess., showed in that she sometimes refused to speak or that she made remarks with the intention to hurt other people, or even attacked them. In the case of Co., the negativism shows in her always uttering the same phrases and not coming out of this attitude. In the case of Cha., we find his great resistance in the muscles. These are different degrees of dissociation and very likely each degree of dissociation has some special relation to a special brain apparatus; the deeper the degree of dissociation, the more primitive, the more deep lying is the apparatus of motility. I may recall in connection with the case Cham., that in decerebrate animals, according to the excellent researches of Bazett and Penfield, we find reactions which are sometimes like the reactions of an emotion. Bazett and Penfield call these reactions "pseudo-affective movements of the animals." When one attempts to wash him, the animal takes on an attitude of resistance and resents it. It behaves in a similar way when it is fed; one gets the impression of a real emotion, but Bazett and Penfield have the feeling that a real emotion could not exist in these animals where a transsection has been made between the corpus quadrigeminum anterius and posterius. This is an unsettled question. We know very little of what is going on in any animal. We know even less of what is going on in the decerebrate animal. I rather believe that these deep centers in the brain stem must have something to do with the emotional life. We could perhaps say that negativism and dissociation in the motility have at least some cortical apparatus, some thalamic apparatus, some striopallidal apparatus, some apparatus in the brain stem. Very likely in every emotion and in every movement all these apparatuses are at work but it might be that the relations between the action of the centers are different in the various cases. To repeat: in the case Co., the thalamo-cortical relation is in some way changed, whereas very likely in a case like Cham., the striopallidal and the brain cortex relation has undergone some change. This is a hypothesis, but I think it is rather good to have hypotheses one can work with. These pictures we see in schizophrenia must have relations to the pictures we see in the course of the development of a child. And it is, therefore, very interesting from this point of view to study the motor development of a child. We see, for instance, that the neck reflex and the righting reflex in the first months of a child are better developed than later. We see that the infant's movements are very much akin to the movements of the choreic. We see that in later development there is some lack of grace and some difficulty in coördination of the movements. All these problems are problems for which there are no definite solutions, but we shall consider the schizophrenic motility as an expression of schizophrenic emotions, and we shall know that the emotions go on on different psychic levels, with different degrees of regression, and that we also can consider the motility from a similar point of view.

CHAPTER XIII

CATALEPSY, MOTOR TROUBLES AND PERSONALITY

Up to the present time, we have not spoken of one phenomenon which occurs in many of these schizophrenic patients and which has also occurred in the patient Hask., whom I shall now discuss. This is the phenomenon of catalepsy. We have to ask what it might mean. From a purely descriptive point of view, there exist very different kinds of catalepsy. First, a catalepsy which is based on a minimum degree of muscular tension so that the arm can remain in its position. The best instance of such a kind of tension is the catalepsy we might observe in hypnotized patients. In the hypnotized person, this catalepsy does not mean merely a muscular state, but it also means that the patient lets the hypnotizer do whatever he wishes to do with his body. It is the expression of a passivity. Hypnotic catalepsy is still related to special apparatuses which go into action when agonistic and antagonistic muscles act at the same time, *e.g.,* in striopallidal lesions. In some cases of encephalitis, very similar phenomena can be observed. In all such cataleptic phenomena there is not only the factor that there is a muscle tonus of a special type, but there is also a lack of impulses. Without the lack of impulses, we would never get the catalepsy. In a case of parietal tumor, I observed in this clinic, with Oedegaard, such a catalepsy was also to be observed partly in connection with the muscle tonus, partly in connection with the general lack of impulses which was obvious in this case. But this lack of impulse did not hinder increased impulses in the special spheres of the neck reflex, and the turning around the longitudinal axis. We shall also consider that in every case of catalepsy we have not only a change in the tonus, but we have also a change in the impulse, and that makes it clear that the psychic factors play such an important part in the genesis of the cataleptic phenomena and that we can provoke cataleptic phenomena by hypnosis. Catalepsy will also be found in states where some general troubles of consciousness exist. We know that in the so-called mental confusion which the Viennese writers call Amentia, we very often find cataleptic phenomena and these are certainly partly in connection with troubles in consciousness which these patients also usually show.

This is the first type of catalepsy. In addition to this, there is another type of catalepsy which is related to a strong innervation of the muscles. In these patients we can see that the agonistic and the antagonistic muscles are innervated at the same time in a very strong way, and very often we find in these patients that the catalepsy is connected with a remarkable degree of negativism, which once broken leads to a fixation of the position which is given in a passive way to the patient. We find then the same queer mixture we have seen in the movements of the patient Co., that she obeys, commands on the one hand, and on the other hand is negativistic. These queer mixtures between obeying and resisting are also to be found in those negativistic cataleptic cases which also present a rather strong stiffness in the muscles. It is rather interesting to see that these patients sometimes not only resist but sometimes immediately begin to strike out against the examiner. Also in these cases, where there are such great muscular tensions, the psychic factor is of an enormous importance. I remember such a case which I observed several months with the greatest negativistic tension I have ever seen. Her body was absolutely stiff. Agonists and antagonists were innervated at the same time. Whenever one tried to change her position, she began to strike at the physician and afterwards remained again stiff and without any movements. If I succeeded in bringing her arm into a new position it remained so.

There are many variations of these two types. In the first type, it happens very often that the extremities remain only a very short time in the given posture and then sink down. It may also happen that there are only special postures which are maintained. One often speaks of pseudo-catalepsy. But pseudo-catalepsy and true catalepsy are identical in their essence. Rigid catalepsy is, as I have mentioned, accompanied by and even substituted for active resistance. I may remind you again that some cataleptic patients, having abandoned their position, afterwards resume their position by their own impulse. Therefore, we can never believe that these muscular phenomena are purely segmental. These are always phenomena which in some way are in connection with psychic factors; with the disintegration and the regression of the whole personality. And here I come back to the important question whether in these states the single muscle-groups are involved in a different way or whether, in order to speak with Kempf, they are involved in special segments. Whenever we have a deep regression before us, we can never expect that anything in the make-up of the personality is absolutely unchanged. We cannot have in the one case only oral erotism increased. The change in the oral erotism brings with it so many changes in the psychic structure. Whenever such a serious dissociation in the impulses occurs, there must be also a dissociation of the whole personality and a falling back to a more primitive stage. But we may consider that the individual life experience has stressed special muscle groups. When a dissociation occurs these groups of muscles are particularly affected, quite in the same way as life experiences may determine the point of fixation. In addition to this individual experience which stresses particular groups of muscles, we have to suppose that every kind of erotism is connected with special muscle groups. On the other hand, every movement and every muscle has its own psychology. We know, for instance, that in a catatonic stupor the eye muscles act in a very different way from the other muscles. One sees sometimes patients with a rather rigid face and yet their eyes are rather vivid and show curiosity, shyness, or other emotions. There are of course many connections with oral tendencies of a rather different type and many of these patients will show some special posture of the mouth, as Kempf especially has emphasized. In the material, I have observed I have never found a special relation between the position of the mouth and the whole make-up of the personality. But such a thing may occur as Kempf supposes. I would, however, never expect that in such a case there would be only the trouble in the segmental functions of the mouth. That there is a general relation of negativism to the jaw I have mentioned already. Of course, some of the muscles of the body are also in a special way in connection with the emotions, especially the muscles of the neck. But whenever we find great changes in one group of the muscles, we should not expect to find other muscles completely free from these changes.

All these regressions to a deeper level of the motor sphere also affect the vegetative sphere. It can thus be understood that in one of our cases we have seen troubles in the pupillary reactions. These pupillary reactions belonging to the unstriped muscles, are nearer to the vegetative system than are the other muscles. In connection with motor regression, we very often find changes in the secretion of the sebaceous glands and sometimes the face of those patients reminds one very much of the face of the post-encephalitic cases. We also find well marked vasomotor troubles of a similar type. In rare cases, the increased volume of the brain leads to choked discs. It is in connection with the vegetative system. It is also of interest to study the pulse reaction of catatonic patients. One finds very often patients who have a very slow pulse rate. The pulse goes down to thirty-six, as I have seen it in one case, but a pulse rate of about fifty is not at all rare. When one takes these patients out of bed, the pulse rate increases with great rapidity. One then sees pulse rates of 140. This great contrast in the pulse of the lying and the standing patients is characteristic. When we find in one field of the organism a deep regression, we do not expect that the rest of the organism will be quite unchanged. In some of these cases, we find symptoms which point to a lesion of the system of the glands of internal secretion (see the next case). Of course the relation between the vegetative system and the glandular system of internal secretion is of a double type. On the one hand, it is maintained that the glands of internal secretion have an influence on the vegetative system, and on the contrary that the vegetative system influences the glands of internal secretion. Sometimes it will be very difficult to decide where the primary lesion is located. But here we consider the symptoms of the vegetative system as well as the glandular system as signs of a regression to the deeper parts of the brain.

These are the problems of the motor part of the catatonic and we now can give a general outline of what troubles can occur in these cases. We have as the first group, the hyperkinetic cases. In the hyperkinetic cases, we find active voluntary movements of various types. Beside voluntary active movements, we find movements the purpose of which is rather unclear. Instinctive half conscious movements prevail. Among these we find many stereotyped tendencies of a more automatic type. Then there are the different types of perseveration and iteration. In all these movements, increased righting reflexes and postural reflexes may come out, which one finds by special examinations, as the basis of more complicated attitudes.

The hyperkinesis can be a hyperkinesis of the whole body, or only of some parts of the body. The hyperkinesis of speech and of the other parts of the body are often dissociated, even hyperkinesis of speech and of the muscles of the mouth region. Among troubles of the akinetic type, we find stupors without rigidity and catalepsy. There are cataleptic stupors either with a minimum of tension or with rigidity and these lead then to negativistic stupors, where the tendency of resistance is the most striking phenomenon.

Hyperkinesis and akinesis are not opposites. Very often they are mixed with one another. There are also many signs which are common to the hyperkinetic as well as to the akinetic phenomena. Also the mannerisms and grimaces about which I spoke in the last lecture and all the troubles which are in connection with the lack of grace. Both groups of patients often have the feeling in common that all the things going on in the motility are not in connection with their personality and are only somatic symptoms. But sometimes both groups feel as if they act the disease and that they could give up their motor symptoms if they wished to. This is an incomplete classification of what we call catatonic phenomena. We can bring all these symptoms in connection with the organic apparatus of the brain. We find the brain stem at first involved; the organic phenomenon is the change in the righting reflex. Secondly, the optic thalamus, the organic phenomenon, is the change in the emotions, the emotional attitudes and the emotional expression. Thirdly, a striopallidal system, of which the organic phenomena are the different types of muscular tension. To the system of the striopallidum belongs also the system of the substantia nigra and of the corpus subthalamicum. Finally (fourth), the system of the cortex. The organic phenomena of that type would be the influence on the righting reflexes and the phenomena relating to apraxia. In many apractic cases, we find cataleptic and akinetic symptoms too. In the so-called cortical apraxia, we find stiffness as mannerisms and lack of grace. But the so-called cortical apraxia has very close relation to the subcortical apparatus too.

There are some other organic phenomena which offer analogies to the phenomena of the catatonics, especially the choreic-athetoid movements with their relation to the system of the striopallidum and cerebellum. The grasping reflex, with its relation to the frontal lobe, and very likely also to the striopallidal system.

This is the general scheme we make use of in order to get an approach to the motor phenomena of catatonia, and we shall now finally try to correlate these ideas again in a special case.

This is the case of Mrs. Hask. The patient is twenty-eight years old. An important point in her psychic life is that she has two step-children but no children of her own. She has wished very much to get children. There is also another difficulty in her life. Her husband was compelled to live in another city than where she lived. The patient complained very much that she was troubled by sex desires she could not satisfy. Once her menstruation was delayed. She began to believe that she was pregnant and announced that she would get twins. The delay in her menstruation may have been caused by the wish to be pregnant. A psychogenic cessation of the menses is a rather common symptom. There also might be some primary trouble in the glandular system of the patient, and this may have helped so that she regressed rapidly to a rather primitive level. At any rate the patient later on developed rather marked troubles in the glandular system. She presented hyperthyroidism and was operated upon. We must consider the special relation between this hyperthyroidism and her psychosis. The interpretation is possible that the hyperthyroidism is one of the causes of her psychosis. It is also possible that the psychosis plays a part in the genesis of the hyperthyroidism. These changes in the diencephalon about which I have spoken are, very often, also changes connected with the glands of internal secretion. Histological changes in the glands of internal secretions have often been found in catatonics, especially increased connective tissue. But it is very difficult to say what is the real significance of these slight changes. But I do not wish to study this side of the question. I want to go deeper into the problem of her motility. The patient began to masturbate, was careless and untidy, and finally she passed into a deep stupor. In the stupor she made some exaggerated movements, but these movements were rather rigid. When I saw her the first time she was rather akinetic with cataleptic symptoms. The catalepsy was of a mixed type. Some tensions were present but the tensions varied very often, and sometimes went into negativism. From the time I first saw the patient, she has had athetoid movements of the fingers. The movements were of a rather slow type. Of course, the patient has not had real athetosis, but the similarity between those tensions and the movements of athetoid patients is rather great, and I cannot believe that such a similarity is mere chance. During the whole course of the psychosis and during the whole observation, the patient has never lost these movements in the fingers. Most of her motor symptoms persisted a very long period varying only in intensity. Of course, it is possible, even probable, that such motor symptoms might have had primarily the value of an expression, and afterwards lost the value of an expression and became automatic. Some of the wild movements of the patient at the beginning of her psychosis were movements which gave the impression of intercourse or labor. At the beginning of such a psychosis, the connection between the motor phenomena and the psychic content is a very clear one. The motor phenomena grow more automatic as the clear connection disappears. We find quite a similar development in the hallucinations. The patient presented religious ideas and that peculiar type of transference, that she had seen me and God creeping into her body. She had not only visual hallucinations but also auditory ones. They were mostly short sentences or even single words hard to understand, but it appears that the voice spoke at first in a rather sensible and complete sentence. These sentences degenerated only in the course of time into a hardly intelligible formula. When in business life, a company has a long name, the first letters of every word may form a new word or parts of the words are omitted, one says for instance for Standard Oil Corporation of New York, Socony. Also, the famous President Schreber, a schizophrenic, who wrote a famous autobiography about his schizophrenic troubles, heard voices which in the beginning had a clear meaning, but finally they spoke in some abbreviations and it was difficult even for him to find out what their real meaning was. We deal with general tendencies in the psychic life. We wish to mechanize what once had a real meaning. In that way, by the way, we can understand the genesis of organs of the organism. The organism produces tools in order not to be compelled again and again to a psychic effort. What once has been an expression becomes finally an automatic movement, a mannerism or stereotyped movement (*cf.* also Kläsi). I have stressed that we shall never understand the motor problems of the schizophrenic if we do not compare the motor problems of the schizophrenics with psychological problems. At the beginning of the psychosis, the patient was found very often in the fetal position, arms, legs and trunk flexed. Of course, it is hardly possible to say what makes the patient take such a position. It may be with the tendency of withdrawing, of sleep, but maybe she identifies herself with the twins she wants to have. That is an open question. Such an exaggerated embryonic position can also be studied from a purely neurological point of view. We must not forget that the fetal position is the opposite of that of decerebrate rigidity. It is remarkable that the patient after the operation on the thyroid retained this fetal position. But she began to give up her akinesis. She tried to get out of bed without changing the position of her legs. Again a very interesting dissociation. On the one hand, she was akinetic concerning her foetal position. Besides this she had many motor impulses. The impulses of the different levels often interfere with each other.

A little later the patient offered a different picture. She always ran around in the ward, and it was hardly possible to keep her quiet, and at the same time she was very rigid. At that time she often fell because there was a discrepancy between her increased tendency to movements on the one hand and this rigidity of the muscles on the other. Of course, one might say that there was a difference between the psychic impulse of running around and the non-psychically-determined rigidity. I should not like to give such a formulation. I should say that very likely the stiffness as well as the running around has a psychic component. I would, therefore, say that the motilities of different levels interfere. I personally think that the problem of interference of the impulses of the different levels is one of the most interesting of psychiatry as well as neurology. The problem of stammering belongs to this group. We cannot understand stammering if we do not realize that there is a person who speaks more quickly than the articulatory apparatus can follow. Something similar happens in cases of encephalitis when the articulatory apparatus has undergone some change and the impulses are not accommodated to the different states of the motor apparatus. And most of the methods by which stammering is treated try to coördinate the tempo to the impulses of the articulatory apparatus. The interference of the motor impulses of the different levels has also been observed by Gerstmann and by me in a postencephalitic child. It had increased impulses of running around. At the same time the innervations sometimes suddenly stopped; she lost tonus and fell down. These sudden losses of tonus interfered with the increased motility and this produced a very peculiar unique picture.

When one sees the photographs of this patient, one sees the lack of grace, the stiffness of the patient which was connected with negativistic tendencies. The patient sometimes had a phenomenon which was not so different from the grasping reflex, whenever the inner part of her hand was touched, she grasped the object and did not let loose. She also followed objects sometimes and tried to grasp them. But, of course, this phenomenon was not so stereotyped as in purely " organic " conditions.

In some phases of the psychosis, the patient complained about her disease of the thyroid, but she did not feel that there was any thing wrong with her psychic attitude. But in the later phases when she got psychically much more free, she complained about stiffness. She brought the stiffness in connection with a great sex excitement and reported also that her first attacks of stiffness before she came to the hospital were in connection with a great sex excitement and a great longing. I shall speak about it later. I wish only to say that catatonic patients very often feel their motor symptoms are in some way peripheral to their personality and purely organic. They belong to a deeper level of the personality. The higher levels of the personality do not agree and therefore these tendencies to stiffness are considered by the patient as purely organic. They do not want to have them in themselves and try to project them into the periphery of their personality. Projection not only takes place in the different layers of the single personality. Sometimes when one is shaken by an intense emotion, one tries to convince oneself that there is no real emotion at all and that the events do not touch our real personality. One tries to project from the center to the periphery. If somebody has a psychic problem, he feels it often in the way that he is extremely tired and nervous. We deal here with another type of projection. All that is going on in the neurasthenic is, therefore, a projection of something that goes on in the central part of the personality into the periphery. Of course, the most successful attempt of doing so is the hysterical symptom. It can be considered as a successful projection from the psychic life into the body and if it is true that one or another internal disease is the expression of our psychic problems—and Jelliffe has held some such opinion for certain organic disturbances—we could say getting an internal disease is a still more successful projection than getting a hysterical symptom. We shall now understand it better when we hear from a catatonic patient that he considers his symptoms as purely organic.

The sex excitement of our patient is in connection with her stiffness. Of course, the sex excitement as such does not give us a sufficient explanation for the catatonic stiffness, because we have the opinion that the catatonic stiffness is very likely not an expression of a purely genital tendency. All that we know about the psychology of catatonia speaks against this. The problem, what kind of motility is connected with the different partial desires of sexuality, is certainly also interesting from the neurological point of view. The problem of the motility of intercourse (which has something to do with the problem of hysterical fit and may be on a more organic line with the problem of the epileptic fit), has not been studied sufficiently as yet. It may be when there is a dissociated motility as in such a case, the sex excitement may only produce the tonic part of the motility of the intercourse. We have to consider that of course when we make a study of the catatonic motility such a study will always be only one-sided because the catatonic motility cannot be separated from the rest of the psychic life of the catatonic. We have also to consider the other problems and, of course, then we shall see that the problems of the motility and the problems of the emotions of the schizophrenic are not so different from each other. Both are life problems.

BIBLIOGRAPHY

Only a small part of the enormous literature is mentioned. The psychoanalytical literature is annotated in my " Introduction to a Psychoanalytic Psychiatry." Translation by B. Glueck. Nervous and Mental Disease Monograph, series No. 50. A part of the neurological literature is annotated in " Die Lagereflexe des Menschen " by Hoff and Schilder, Wien, Springer, 1927.

BAZETT AND PENFIELD. A Study of the Sherringtons Decerebrate Animal in the Chronic and Acute Condition. Brain, 45, 1922.

BENEDEK. Zwangsmässiges Schreien in Anfällen. Zentralbl. f. Neurol. u. Psychiatrie, 98, 1925.

BLEULER. Zur Theorie des schizophrenen Negativismus. Psychiatrisch-Neurologische Wochenschrift, 12, No. 18–21.

GUTTMANN. Zur Kasuistik und Pathogenese des Reflexverlustes bei funktionellen Erkrankungen. Ztschr. f. Neurol., 115, 1928.

HAENEL, J. Neurologische Erscheinungen bei Schizophrenien. Klin. Wochenschr. 7.

HOFF UND SCHILDER. Haltungs- und Stellreflexe bei katatonen Bewegungsstörungen. Wiener med. Wochenschr., 1927.

HOMBURGER. Ueber die Entwickelung der menschlichen Motorik und ihrer Beziehung zu den Bewegungsstörungen der Schizophrenien. Z. Neurol., 78, 1922.

HOMBURGER. Zur Gestaltung der normalen menschlichen Motorik und ihrer Beurteilung. Z. Neurol., 85, 1923.

JUNG. Kritik von Bleulers: Zur Theorie der schizophrenen Negativismus. Jahrbuch f. Psychoanalyse, 3.

JELLIFFE. Mental Pictures in Schizophrenia and Epidemic Encephalitis. Amer. Jour. of Psychiat., 6, 1927. Post-encephalitic Respiratory Disorders. Monograph No. 49, 1927.

KLEIST. Gegenhalten (motorischer Negativismus), Zwangsgreifen und Thalamus opticus. Monatsschr. f. Neurol. u. Psychiat., 65, 1927.

KLEIST. Bewegungsstörungen und Bewegungsleistungen der Stammganglien des Gehirns. Naturwissenschaft, 15, 1928.

MERZBACH. Die Sprachiteration und ihre Lokalisation bei Herderkrankungen des Gehirns. Journ. f. Neurol. u. Psychiat., 36, 1928.

MEYER, A. Zur pathologischen Anatomie der epidemischen Metencephalitis. Z. Neurol., **80**, 1927.

POLLAK UND SCHILDER. Zur Lehre von den Sprachantrieben. Z. Neurol., **104**, 1926.

SCHALTENBRAND. Normale Bewegungs- und Lagereaktionen bei Kindern. Deutsche Ztschr. f. Nervenhk., **87**, 1925.

SCHALTENBRAND. Die Beziehungen extrapyramidaler Symptomenkomplexe zu den Lage- u. Bewegungsreaktionen. Ibid. **108**, 1929.

SPIEGEL UND GOLDBLOOM. Die Körperhaltung im Zustand der sogenannten Hypnose der Säugetiere. Pflügers Arch. f. Physiol., **69**, 1921.

STENGEL UND SCHILDER. Schmerzasymbolie. Z. Neurol., **113**, 1928.

STENGEL UND SCHILDER. Der Hirnbefund bei Schmerzasymbolie. Klin. Wochenschr., 1928.

WESTPHAL, A. Ueber Pupillenphaenomen bei Encephalitis epidemica. Z. Neurol., **68**, 1921.

(Literatur über Pupillenphaenomen—Kehrer : Pathologie der Pupillenbewegung. Z. Neurol., **87**, 1923.)